HOW TO
Worship
the Goddess

&

KEEP YOUR BALLS

A Man's Guide to Sacred Sex

How to

Worship

the Goddess

&

KEEP YOUR BALLS

DAVID BRUCE LEONARD

Roast Duck Producktion

ISBN# 978-0-9800505-3-0

david@davidbruceleonard.com
http://www.davidbruceleonard.com

Just what you need... another

Roast Duck Producktion

*A peasant must stand a long time on a hillside with his
mouth open before a roast duck flies in."*

CHINESE PROVERB

For those Men who are my friends.
You know who you are.

Tell a wise person, or else keep silent,
because the massman will mock it right away.
I praise what is truly alive,
what longs to be burned to death.
In the calm water of love-nights,
where you were begotten, where you have begotten,
a strange feeling comes over you
when you see the silent candle burning.
Now you are no longer caught
in the obsession with darkness,
and a desire for higher love-making
sweeps you upward.
Distance does not make you falter,
now, arriving in magic, flying,
and, finally, insane for the light,
you are the butterfly and you are gone.
And so long as you haven't experienced
this: to die and so to grow,
you are only a troubled guest
on the dark earth.

—GOETHE

Contents

Acknowledgments

I wish to thank those who have helped in some way with this manuscript:

Dr. Mitchell V. Brinks, MD, MPH
Christy Collins, Book Cover/Interior Designer
Kornelia DeKorne
Stacy Domer
Dr. Sherellen Gerhart, MD
Cheryl Ginter
Stacey Guss
Auntie Hosebag
Jen Hoy
Renee Jeffus
Nancy Kahalewai, Publisher
Amara Karuna
Kevin "Rio" Kiper, L.Ac.
Malia Laurelin
Rich Lipset
Lea Marzetta
Janet Meredith, L.Ac.
Graham & Joy Silbermann
Amanda Spaur
M. Stone, Illustrator
Goddess Unfolding
German E. Velasco

Medical and Therapeutic Disclaimer

The exercises described in this book can be extremely strenuous and should only be attempted by someone in good physical condition. If you are unsure about your ability to safely perform these exercises then consult your physician before attempting anything described in this book.

A lot of the exercises described herein involve oil. Oil on slippery surfaces is dangerous. If you are unsure about the safety of any of these exercises do not attempt to do them. Use your good judgment and common sense.

This book is for informational purposes only. It is not a substitute for medical care or psychotherapy. If you are in need of medical care or psychological support you should see a licensed professional.

Preface

The assumptions from which this book proceeds:

1) Any pleasure we experience that is not derived from the suffering of another sentient being is good for us. It is good for us physically, emotionally, and spiritually.

2) Sexual pleasure is good. Sexual pleasure is a great gift, and it exists for far more reasons than just procreation.

3) *Any* private non-coercive activity between consenting adults is solely their concern.

❧ All of the perceptions in the first part of this book come from my observations and experiences as well as the observations and experiences of others. I share what I have seen and what has worked for me in my life. What works for me may not work for you. This type of introspection is not for everyone, and it may not be for you. So I would encourage you to use what works for you, and to leave the rest behind.

❧ As men, we are all prone to self-delusion and the avoidance of accountability, and I am no exception. Some of the lessons contained herein have come easily to me but most have been difficult and painful. I now see this process of self-confrontation as the path of the warrior, where the battle is waged inside and my enemy is my own laziness and self-delusion.

❧ The second part of this book, titled "Rivers of Love", is an eclectic system of healing based on traditional Daoist observations about the nature of health, sexuality, and healing. While almost all the material in Rivers of Love is based on the age-old *principles* of traditional Chinese medicine and Daoist longevity practices, some of the *techniques* are not traditional. I have given them Daoist names and used Chinese medical terminology in order to keep them congruent with the Daoist concepts and practices from which they are derived.

❧ The word "fuck" is used in this book in a very specific way. While I am aware that this will offend some people it is not my intention to be offensive. I use the word to denote an inner acceptance and embrace of the healthy aggression sometimes inherent in human sexual interaction.

❧ While this book is primarily directed toward heterosexual couples, many of the ideas and practices herein can easily be applied to other types of relationships. We should love whomever we choose, but we should love well. The dynamics of human emotional-sexual interactions are universal. You'll figure it out.

❧ The title and theme of this book is obviously tongue-in-cheek. While I write extensively about "Worshipping the Goddess", the reader should understand that this work is really about mutuality. When we are "Worshipping the Goddess", we are not worshipping *our partner* per se; we are worshipping the sacred feminine essence that resides within her, *and* in us. In addition, it is just as important to *be worshipped* by our partner, as it is to *worship* her. Mutuality is crucial for any relationship. That I have focused so much on *our* accountability as men is because ultimately the only behavior that we men can really control is our own, not hers. We can still hold her to high standards however, the same standards that we expect of ourselves. We must always hold her accountable for her behavior.

❧ The second part of this book is for men who enjoy giving pleasure to women or men who want to learn how to give pleasure to women. That I have left out the Rivers of Love material for *women worshipping men* is an unfortunate by-product of the theme of this book. Rest assured, the upcoming book *Rivers of Love: Sexuality in the Heart of Healing* will have extensive instructional material on how our partners may worship us.

❧ And finally, this work is a combination of psycho-emotional observations on one hand, and specific sexual, massage, and/or breathing techniques on the other. We cannot be good partners without doing our work, and ultimately we cannot be good lovers without being good partners. When we walk into our bedroom with our beloved we cannot separate our physiology from our breathing, our breathing from our emotions, or our emotions from our sexuality. The divisions between such things are as arbitrary as the chapters in this book. I have joined them together here because I feel that they are all different manifestations of the same great mystery, the deep potential wisdom inherent in human sexual relationships. If we are to uncover this wisdom we will need to integrate all aspects of our health and emotions with our sexuality. May we unravel the mystery and uncover the potential for a significant and fulfilling relationship with our partner.

Virility is the capacity to marvel.

Tantric Text

Introduction

If you are like me, you're probably sort of attached to your balls. I mean, you'd prefer to keep them where they are, maybe even *use* them once in a while.

Keeping your balls while worshipping the Goddess is extremely difficult. It may well be the most difficult thing you have ever done. Keeping your balls with a heart-pounding female gnawing at your soul and *begging* you to love her, to *fuck* her, to *devour* her, will not be easy.

Keeping your balls while worshipping the Goddess will mean facing the worst enemy you have ever encountered in your life—a hideous, nasty and cruel creature who will go to any lengths to deceive you, to keep you from your happiness.

Who is this enemy? Is it some castrating female? Some dangerous Lolita? Is it an evil seductive vagina with sharp teeth, drawing you in, *seducing you,* only to then rip out your heart, and God knows *what* else?

No, nothing like that. *If only it were that easy.*

OK, here we go....

Pick up a mirror.

Really… Pick up a mirror and take a good *long* look. Your enemy is in this mirror. The enemy in this mirror is *you*.

I know… *I know.* Sorry about that. Wouldn't it be better to have a *different* mirror? A mirror that makes you *look* and *feel* fantastic? Like one of those old curved carnival mirrors… only in reverse. Sort of like digital enhancement for your self-image, air brushing for your soul.

But what about that girlfriend who totally *adored* you. Remember her? Oh… *my… God….* remember how she *admired* you? Now *that's* a mirror.

Or how about that one woman you slept with last spring? Remember how she clawed your back as she climaxed and *screamed* how you were the *best* lover she'd *ever* had? Remember how *powerful* you felt?

Well… first the bad news. This book will not make you a better lover. This book will not improve your sex life, blow sunshine up your ass or tell you how wonderful you are. This book will not give you a bigger penis, "six-pack abs" or teach you "How to Pick Up Chicks". If that is what you are looking for, put this book down right now and *run, don't walk*, to your nearest carnival mirror or *Damsel in Distress*.

If this book does its job, it will encourage you to look into *another* mirror. This other mirror is *very* deep… and *much* darker. This other mirror will not make you feel better about yourself. In fact, it will make you feel worse. You will feel worse before you feel better.

But now, the good news. This mirror is the greatest gift you will ever receive. Others can lead you to it, but you alone must look into it. As a matter of fact, this mirror becomes a mirror *only* when you look into it. I cannot give this mirror to you; only your partner can do that. At first you will *hate* this mirror. You will swear that the mirror is a liar. But the irony is, you're *supposed* to hate this mirror. If you don't hate this mirror, then *something is wrong*. If you're not humbled and at least mildly embarrassed, then you are probably looking into that *other* mirror, the carnival mirror. Sorry, wrong mirror. But if you can muster the courage to be a Man and to accept the truth of your life, then you will accept this mirror, and reclaim your balls. And, ironically, if you finally and fully reclaim your balls, then you will *seek out this mirror.* You will seek out this mirror because your balls will tell you: *This mirror is your way home.*

As I said, this book will not make you a better lover. But if you are diligent and self-reflective, then this book may help you become a better Man. That new Man might, in turn, *look into this mirror, listen to his partner,* and then teach you how to be a *much* better lover.

If you want to worship the Goddess but still keep your balls, you'd better be prepared to face the enemy in the mirror. But be forewarned, he's *much* nastier than you are.

WHAT DOES IT MEAN TO WORSHIP THE GODDESS?

To worship the Goddess is to enter divinity in a human form. To feel silk penetrate us. To feel goodness permeate our cells.

To worship the Goddess is to honor trees and branches, limbs and flowers. And roots. To stand in awe of stars and see Her spanning across the heavens. To find goodness in a woman who is strong and fragile. To love her when she may not even love herself. To look for the best in her but still hold her accountable.

To worship the Goddess is to understand that a relationship is a garden that has two gardeners, but that it can perish if either fails to abide. To recognize that seeds planted often sprout; and that shit, properly used, creates flowers.

To worship the Goddess is to become a fish that had never known it was thirsty.

To worship the Goddess is to sacrifice our vanity for humility, to offer ourselves in service to a unique and dangerous process. To place ourselves on the brazier of love and pain, and to be annealed and purified by that fire.

To worship the Goddess is to embrace her humanness, and our own. To understand that her happiness is inexorably linked with ours.

To worship the Goddess is to wash her feet, to stroke her head, to kiss her flower as if we were kissing her mouth. To worship the Goddess is to *adore* her with our hands, to withhold our erotic gratification and transmute it in order to exalt both of our spirits.

To worship the Goddess is to be angry when we are bleeding and we see that she holds the knife. To worship the Goddess is to hold her up when we are too weak to do so. To worship the Goddess is to clutch her flesh as if we were hanging off her cliff and watch in horror as our fingers peel away. To worship the Goddess is to look into her eyes and love her through the smoke of our rage, our torrents of grief, and the dark poisoned shimmering of our mother's fears. To worship the Goddess is to see her fragility, as we hate her. To worship the Goddess is to free her when we cannot be consoled, to pick ourselves up, wounded and shaking, slowly taking small broken steps through our pain and toward our healing.

To worship the Goddess is to know that we need her but *we can never own her*. We offer our bone-racking ecstasy up on an altar of gold and tarnished dreams and bitter herbs.

To worship the Goddess is to take ourselves by the balls and go inside, alone, to work through the dark painful retching that drives us. To worship the Goddess is to transform ourselves into something *worthy* of sacrifice. To be strong when we don't want to be, vulnerable when we don't want to be, but always keeping a candle burning inside for ourselves. It is said that only a God can truly worship a Goddess.

Yes, we are our own way home, but her mirror can illuminate our path.

WHY DO WE WORSHIP THE GODDESS?

We worship the Goddess to pull the damaged parts of ourselves into union, to melt our shattered hearts, to share a soul embrace on this brief and lonely journey.

Women are the only exploited group in history to have been idealized into powerlessness.

<small>ERICA JONG</small>

We worship the Goddess because hundreds of thousands of our sisters, mothers, daughters, and lovers were burned alive for no other reason than being who they were. We worship the Goddess to atone for the countless unspeakable horrors that we, as *men*, have inflicted upon women throughout time. We worship the Goddess because we recognize that in spite of our viciousness, in spite of our madness, *we now make different choices.*

We worship the Goddess because we *must*, because it is who we *are* and who we choose to be. Can we ever really and fully embody our manhood without women? We began this journey from our wounds, but *her fire transforms us.* Through this transformation, we become Men. Her sacred and unflinching mirror sets us free.

We worship the Goddess because she is where we come from; because she is our mother, our daughter, our beloved grandmother; She is this very Earth that embraces our feet. It is She alone that gives life. We worship the Goddess because we love her, and because she can help us find our way home.

PART ONE

Finding and Keeping our Balls

The real accomplishment in life is the art of being a warrior, which is the only way to balance the terror of being a man with the wonder of being a man.

CARLOS CASTANEDA

Establishing our Roots

WHAT DO YOU CARE WHAT OTHER PEOPLE THINK?

We like to believe that we don't care what others think about us, but we do. We care *a lot* what other people think. So does everyone else we know... except for sociopaths. We are *hardwired* to care what other people think. Our antennae are biologically attuned to the outside world, especially other members of our tribe.

Caring about what other people think is not a problem. The problem is *how much* we care. When we care *too much*, our perceptions go out of balance and become deeply skewed. If we are not well rooted in who we are, we become overly concerned about other people's judgments and inordinately influenced by their perceptions. When this happens over time we can habitually smother our core. We train ourselves to ignore or override that faint voice inside, *our voice*. This can happen at such an early age and with such force that we *forget how to access our inner self*. But we can remember; we can find our way home again. We can retrain ourselves to listen to that faint voice.

We can think of this as two different *"frames of reference"*, in other words, two different perspectives from which we experience who we are.

External Frame of Reference: "Honey, can I use the Balls tonight?"

The first frame of reference we call an "external frame of reference". This is also known as the "social mirror" or the "reflected sense of self". As men, we often find ourselves emotionally enmeshed with our partners, yet befuddled as how to navigate those entanglements. This confusion arises from an imbalance in our frames of reference.

Our *external* frame of reference is one of the reasons we humans bond so strongly into tribes. We are designed to bond with others. Our external frame of reference generates doubts about our behavior and ourselves. Those doubts keep us linked to each other and in so doing, keep the "tribe" intact. This is one reason why teenagers are so blatantly concerned with the perceptions of their peers; their insecurity keeps their "tribe" intact. In addition, our ability to see ourselves through the eyes of others is also what allows us to be compassionate and empathic. We can imagine what things are like from their perspective and so we can "put ourselves in their shoes".

While our external frame of reference *tries* to perceive us through other people's eyes, it often perceives us through our *fantasy and fears* of what we *imagine* other people may think of us. In our external frame of reference we create an incessant inner voice that keeps asking, *"How am I doing? How am I doing? How am I doing?"* It constantly seeks reassurance from the outside world that we are okay.

From the time we are children, we are trained to seek most of our validation from the outside world, when ideally most of that validation would come from within; we would be self-validating. This self-validation is our true nature and birthright. But what we do instead is to default to an external frame of reference; we rely on *others* to validate us.

The dissenter is every human being at those moments of his life when he resigns momentarily from the herd and thinks for himself.

ARCHIBALD MACLEISH

For example, in relationship we may need our partner to reflect us in a flattering way in order for us to feel good about ourselves. We may need her to tell us how wonderful we are and to admire our strength. There is nothing wrong with feeling wonderful, strong, and admired, but if we can only generate these feelings from outside ourselves, we are hobbled. If we can only receive nourishment from our partner then we cannot drink from our own well. This obsessive need for validation cuts us off from the rooting we might have in our lives—this idealized version of ourselves. Our soil can only supply us with this nutrition if we live in our integrity and our behavior is aligned with our deepest values. Without integrity and conscious values we have no soil in which to root our lives.

If our partner genuinely cares about us, our constant need for validation can also deny her the opportunity to express herself in a genuine way. Let's face it; she is not going to continually admire us, especially after she gets to know us. If we always need her admiration, there will always be subtle pressure in the relationship for her to reflect back to us a carnival image, this idealized version of ourselves. This pressure may prevent her from speaking her full truth, and we will need to know her full truth if we are going to effectively navigate our relationship.

Sometimes, her less-than-flattering view of us is accurate. Then we are faced with the dilemma of self-honesty, self-delusion, or finding another partner.

Other times she is just upset at us because we are not reflecting back *her* idealized self-image, or her "movie" of what the relationship is "supposed" to look like. If her self-image is at stake, she will often blame us for her own unpleasant reflection. Sometimes she may realize that her values are different than ours and be disappointed. Or we may not live up to her expectations of what she wants in her life or her partner.

In any event, if our partner is not acting in a way that triggers those warm fuzzy feelings and we cannot generate them in ourselves from a place of deep humility and self-acceptance, then we may try to manipulate the situation in order to generate that behavior in her. Or we may withdraw or rail against her, hanging on to our resentment as if it was a life vest. Her less-than-perfect view of us may throw us into a panic. If she sees us as flawed then we might also see ourselves as flawed and then we might be forced to confront painful and unflattering truths about ourselves.

There are two ways that we can generate those warm fuzzy feelings on our own. One way is through the often long and painful process of self-honesty, which leads to self-acceptance and eventually to self-love. This process generates our own deepest values and the recognition of who we are.

The second way to generate those warm fuzzy feelings is to smother our unpleasant realizations with distractions or addictions. This, while occasionally comforting, is not nearly as gratifying in the long run.

If we feel powerless to define the context of our own lives, our masculinity, and the inner richness of our terrain, then we often will default to manipulating others to try to control their behavior. But deep down inside we always know that we are manipulating. When we try to manipulate others we simply climb onto a hamster wheel; it is a dead end…futile and ironic. Ultimately the only thing in this world we can ever really control is our own behavior, not the behavior of others. And our nutrition must come from within; we must uncover the source of our own nourishment. Instead of manipulating others we must take a chance, stumble into the darkness, and try to find our way home.

INTERNAL FRAME OF REFERENCE: COMING HOME TO OURSELVES

The other side of this phenomenon is our internal frame of reference. This internal frame of reference is rooted in the core of who we are *independent* of what others think of us. It is what we think of ourselves. Our internal frame of reference is rooted in our deepest values. We may not know what our deepest values are, but we can all

*When you are content to be
simply yourself and don't
compare or compete,
everybody will respect you.*

LAO TZU

access our core to *some* degree, even if only to connect with a small sliver of ourselves. But even with just this fingernail grip on our center, with tenacity and persistence, we can find our way home. We can think of this internal frame of reference as a muscle that we had long forgotten, therefore seldom used. Once we know it's there, we can strengthen it, and that strength will build on itself.

But in order for us to access this internal frame of reference, we must push through the numbness that we have created in our chests as boys and young men. We have to overcome the fear of discovering who we are. In order to integrate and return home through the fog of our lives, we have to know what we are feeling.

Boys don't cry... is that true? No, it's not true. Actually boys *do* cry... and for very good reasons. We need no justification to shed tears, to feel our own bodies. Could anything be more obvious? We cry because we have feelings that move us. To cry is to embrace our humanity, to sink our fingers deep into our own soil. The only boys who don't cry are those who are strangers to themselves, those whose parched roots have long ago been ripped out of their Earth. The boys who don't cry have a hell of a long journey ahead of them if they ever want to find their way home again.

Essentially, we have two choices: We can compartmentalize or we can integrate. We can fracture ourselves into pieces and stuff our bloody shards into cold metal drawers or we can finally and fully have the courage to embrace who we are. We can find the courage to wrap ourselves around our humanity, our rich humanity that always pushes through, beyond the pounding of our insane guilt hammers and the crippling shredding of our shame. We can send these foolish cartoons of perfection back where they came from. Our perfection, the real perfection of our humanity, comes from using our flaws as signposts, using our pain as a Geiger counter, allowing the best of our humanness to arise without denying the worst. We can reclaim the fertile and fecund ground of being from which we emerge. We can reclaim the rich darkness of our feminine nature while still illuminating our manhood.

Without an emotional connection to our core, we cannot root properly in ourselves, nor can we show our sons how to do it. Our rooting is visceral. We feel it in our bodies and it is as unmistakable as an orgasm. But it is personal and difficult to describe to someone who has not experienced it. Once this rooting happens, once we come home to ourselves, we find balance between our frames of reference and it changes our lives forever.

FINDING BALANCE BETWEEN THE FRAMES OF REFERENCE

Both of these internal and external frames of reference are crucial for our survival. But they must be in balance to maintain health. Just as our bodies must maintain balance in our blood chemistry in order to be healthy, so must our psyches maintain balance in our frames of reference. When they are out of balance our minds can become toxic.

To achieve balance we must create a commitment to balance. But what does that balance look like? In classical martial arts training there is a posture known as a "cat stance" in which 60% of the weight is on the rear leg, and 40% of the weight is on the front. This may embody the ideal balance of internal (rear) and external (front) frames of reference for us as men. If we are 100% "rear weighted", i.e., if we are only rooted in our experience and incapable of a compassionate external frame of reference, then we are a narcissist or a sociopath... otherwise known as a "selfish asshole". Someone with a completely internal frame of reference sees the world only in terms of what they can get from it... what's in it for them. We all know people like that.

On the other hand if we are "front weighted", if we see the world mostly from an external frame of reference, we cannot shift back quickly enough if we need to "defend" ourselves with our hands or our front leg. If we are front weighted we are not rooted in ourselves, we are overly run by how we believe other people perceive us. In other words, we become doormats. And we also know people like that.

A 60/40 ratio of internal to external frame of reference allows us to stay rooted in ourselves with our "rear leg", while still able to feel empathic or defend with our "front leg". To feel our rear leg powerfully root into the earth is to connect with our own emotional body, to anchor our core masculinity, but also to fully anchor in Mother Earth. When we root we return to a place that is profound, visceral, and unmistakable. This internal validation is what we call "coming home". We acknowledge our most subtle sensations and emotions. When we root in ourselves for the first time, we change irrevocably, as do our relationships with others. We begin to see the possibility that we might somehow transcend our scripting, including the very powerful scripts that we have adopted from women.

How Women Wished We Showed Up

In the 1970s and 1980s, as more and more boys in the West were raised by single mothers, there was a strong cultural pressure to raise better men in order to create a better world. Boys conceived in the 1960s were reaching puberty in the 1970s and 1980s, and the gender-neutral paradigms of the idealistic sixties were beginning to manifest. Many young mothers raised their sons to behave and feel the way that they *wished* men behaved and felt: kind, compassionate, considerate, and empathic. Of course we men are capable of manifesting these qualities, but we must manifest them in a masculine way. We cannot manifest them at the expense of our masculinity. It was difficult for young mothers to adequately nurture these qualities in testosterone-addled young males. There are things about being a man that are difficult for women to understand, particularly things involving aggression and sexuality. As young men, with no male around us to model a healthy masculinity, we adopted our mother's perceptions of men and the world. We generated an external frame of reference about what it means to be a man. We had no way to access ourselves internally, and we had no healthy men around to show us how. In attempting to create qualities in ourselves that do

*It does not matter how much you love
someone, you are never going to be
what that person wants you to be...*

Don Miguel Ruiz

not simultaneously embrace our masculinity, we submerge parts of ourselves into shadow. We cannot suppress our masculine nature for very long. Pressure will build. Male energy is, at its core, radiating and penetrating. This energy will radiate and penetrate somehow, either directly or through subterfuge.

Most traditional cultures have rites of passage for young boys, and those rites channel adolescent aggression toward maturing into a healthy masculinity. They are designed to create a healthy manhood well suited for tribal living. In our drive to become "modern", we have abandoned these rites of passage, as they often contain aggressive behavior and physical wounding. In the 1960s, this kind of aggression was frowned upon and seen as an incitement to war. In the absence of rites of passage or healthy male role models, something unfortunate happened. Rather than creating males who were peaceful and compassionate, we have created young males who are passive-aggressive and, at least on the surface, "spiritual". James Hillman called these men *Puer Aeternus*, and Robert Bly called them *Flying Boys*. They are otherwise known as *Peter Pans*.

Peter Pans are men that, in desiring not to "become what they hate", i.e. in trying to avoid becoming "assholes", become soft … at least on the outside. In order to become what women think of as "good" men, they reject their masculinity, including their own direct aggression. They do not want to become like those "other men", the ones who are so obviously screwing up the planet. What they do not understand is that without fully embracing their healthy masculinity, they can never embrace the feminine.

A healthy masculinity is the same quality that draws a line in the sand based on principle. A healthy masculinity values principle over power. A healthy male aggression is energized and has vigor. It is a quality that allows us to hold space, to know who we are, and to create deep commitment. It has tenacity and perseverance. It prevents us from betraying ourselves. It keeps us going even when it would be easier to quit. A healthy aggression is based on deep values, on principles. It sets and holds boundaries. It contains things. It is

When one is pretending,
the entire body revolts.

ANAIS NIN

the quality that gives us the courage to look in the mirror. Without reasonable and healthy aggression, we have no container in which to hold our families and ourselves. Without healthy aggression we become either passive aggressive or we become hostile.

The Flying Boy avoids duties, emotional clarity, and responsibility; he justifies his inadequacies by proclaiming them to be lofty spiritual principles. He *actively* avoids embracing his fiery, aggressive masculine energy. He rejects both his own fire and his "negative" emotions. Of course, neither goes away. He still has to feel negative emotions and his hormones continue to stoke the fire in his belly. In this situation both his fire and his negative emotions come out "sideways"; they are unable to be contained. He still has his testicles, but he cannot access them; he has placed them into a kind of cold storage. He has replaced his backbone with a wishbone. Unable to take a stand for himself, recognize his core values, or set boundaries, he has no choice except to become passive-aggressive.

There is another side to this coin, however. Men in other cultures and subcultures have a different dilemma. These cultures that are more misogynistic and sex negative than ours produce men that are so afraid of women that they actively oppress them. They present an unhealthy aggression, a preemptive aggression that emerges from shadow. This is not Goddess worship; it is thinly veiled fear and hate. These men actually *do* need to get more in touch with their feminine side and to honor the mothers of their children as political and social equals.

But whether *Peter Pan* or *King Kong*, all these men have something in common: They are numb within their own chest. Their grief has been driven underground. What our culture and their cultures do not tell them is that their grief is a door to their healing.

GRIEVING

As men, we need to grieve. Without grief we cannot navigate our emotional bodies.

In Africa, some tribes have ritualized the male grieving experience. The men in these tribes grieve together as ritual, to bond and create unity between them. There is a recognition that men who cannot or do not grieve are cut off from themselves—from the deeper context of their lives. When we are cut off from our source we can become unconscious, disruptive, and dangerous. We try to negotiate our pain by smothering it and driving it deeper into our chest. But we cannot escape from our pain by stuffing it. We must transmute it, and in order to transmute our pain we must feel it. Smothered pain festers. Festering pain will always emerge, somehow. It cannot stay submerged forever. When it does emerge it usually shows up as some sort physical or emotional trauma or "*dis-ease*". On the other hand, through our grieving, we open and awaken our chest. This gives our pain psychological and spiritual air that keeps it from festering.

Short of moving to Africa, there are things we can do in order to keep our emotional bodies healthy enough to periodically grieve. The best way to access grief is the conscious commitment to do so. We need to notice what we are *feeling*; we need to *pay attention*. It helps to give ourselves permission to cry. We can allow ourselves to weep, to be *seen*. Joining with other men and sharing openly can help. This is not about being "sensitive New-Age men", but about seeing the truth. And the truth is that without access to our emotional body, without knowing what we are feeling, we men cannot find our way home.

SHUTTING DOWN FROM THE NECK TO THE NAVEL: "COULD YOU TELL ME WHAT I'M FEELING"?

In some ways men are like lawyers: We need so many lawyers because we have so many lawyers. A woman's dilemma has always been the same, to find a partner strong enough to protect her, but not so violent that she or the children are in danger. A tribe's dilemma has always been the same: "We need these violent young men to protect us, (often from *other* violent young men) *but what the hell do we do with them?*" For hundreds of thousands of years, the stronger and more aggressive males were needed to protect the tribe, to guard the perimeter, and to kill invaders. We had to be physically strong and aggressive enough to hunt down and kill very dangerous animals, and very dangerous men. In order for us, as young men, to be able to do our job, of killing others we had to do *something* with our feelings of empathy. If we were to look an invader in the eye and take his life, then we had to be able to shut down our feelings, to smother our grief. The person we were killing may have been very much like us, with people he loved and perhaps children who loved and needed him. If we were too empathic, we would be unable to take that person's life. If we could not stifle our feelings and take that person's life, we would have put our life and those that we love most at risk. So nature has designed us to shut off from our empathy in order to protect those we love. The genes of our ancestors are still within us. We are designed to shut down and demonize our "enemies" in order to be able to kill them and do our job.

But, as is often the case, there is a trade-off. In order to be able to kill we must cut off our empathy and shut down our emotional bodies, becoming numb in our chests. In doing so, we become trapped. Can we still love our family when our chests are numb? Can we be dead in our chests but still feel our children's hearts beating? Can we really nurture our children and navigate the delicate balance of their emotions without knowing what we're feeling?

Numbing ourselves works well in a time of war, but what about when we are no longer at war? What if we want to *really* make love? Can we *really* make love to her and not know what we are feeling? We may think that we just need sex in order to feel intimacy, but what if we are wrong? What if we *need* her? What if beneath our pain we really want more? What if *real* intimacy scares the shit out of us?

What if the woman we love most in the world needs *more* than just sex from us in order to feel loved? Can we show her who we really are... without fear or pretense? Can we show her who we are if we do not know what we are feeling? What would it be like if we had nowhere to hide? What would it be like if we allowed ourselves

Resilient strength is the opposite of helplessness. The tree is made strong and resilient by its grounded root system. These roots take nourishment from the ground and grow strong. Grounding also allows the tree to be resilient so that it can yield to winds of change and not be uprooted.

PETER LEVINE, AWAKENING THE TIGER

to love her in spite of our fears? What if we could actually show up with *all of ourselves* in relationship?

Our numbed chest can make all this very difficult for us. This evolutionary trade-off is difficult, but that's the hand we've been dealt.

Ultimately we have to take responsibility for how we show up. As men, we are always part of the problem and part of the solution. Which way that scale will tilt is ultimately up to us. If we want to become whole again, then we need to reactivate our emotional bodies, reclaim our emotions and look into that mirror. If not... then we will not come home. We always have a choice: We can remain lost, or we can return home. If we choose to return home, and if we are fortunate, we may find intimacy without enmeshment upon our hearth.

Intimacy Without Enmeshment: A Tree Can Only Spread As Wide As Its Roots.

We cannot be intimate without extending ourselves, without extending our branches. But to extend our branches, to be intimate, is to stand on *very* dangerous ground. To be intimate we must expose ourselves, become vulnerable, and risk rejection. We risk toppling over. We might reveal who we are to our partner and they might not like what they see. True enough. But intimacy cannot exist without vulnerability. This is the risk we must take if we are to be in relationship. We go into relationship with our heart and eyes open. We must be strong, but we must also choose our partner wisely. Ultimately, if we are not willing to risk pain, we should not enter into intimate relationships.

Intimacy also cannot exist without rootedness. To stand on the dangerous ground of intimacy we must be rooted. With rootedness, our vulnerability can also become our strength. The spreading of our branches, the very act that makes us vulnerable, also allows us to receive sunlight and nourishment. But without rooting in our-

*The irony of safety is isolation
and incarceration within oneself.*

SHERELLEN GERHART

selves we cannot extend our branches and reach toward our partner. Without genuine rootedness, self-disclosing becomes much too dangerous. Without genuine rootedness, real intimacy will scare the hell out of us. It will create a visceral repulsion; we will avoid it at any cost because we have no roots, because we have no stability. This repulsion arises from an unwillingness to accept our humanity, to accept ourselves as we truly are. We think that our distance from our partner keeps us safe, but in reality, it just keeps us isolated. If we cannot face who we are, we cannot reveal ourselves to our partner. As we get closer to her, we come closer to seeing ourselves as we are. Looking into the mirror that is generated by our love, the stories we tell ourselves begin to crack and our façade starts to peel. As the mirror gets closer and the threat of true intimacy looms, things begin to crumble. We feel as if we are about to lose our soul.

Enmeshment is the opposite of intimacy. In true intimacy our branches are intertwined but not enmeshed. They touch and nourish each other in many places but they have not grown together. It is our own roots and trunk that hold us up, not our partner's branches. We hold ourselves up and our partner holds herself up. We are here by choice, as is she. When we are enmeshed we are afraid to create roots for ourselves; in order to grow roots we must let go of her branches. Because we have no roots we use our partner's branches to hold us up. We draw on her strength rather than our own. We yearn to be coddled, to be mothered. We avoid responsibility, shifting it onto her.

Of course as partners we will often lean on each other… that is one of the treasures that comes from being in relationship. But that can last only so long before we will need to find our own footing again. Ultimately each of us must hold ourselves up.

We are always capable of rooting in ourselves but it is not an easy process. It can be especially difficult for us to root, to self-source, if we did not have a healthy male that we could model as we were growing up. Most of us did not. So we must either figure out how do it on our own or we must try to find other men who can help us along in the process.

Inevitably, in order to root in ourselves we must extend beyond our comfort zone and embrace those unflattering mirrors. For whatever reason, some of us will never root in ourselves, but our ability to self-source can increase with age. The process of aging seems to help us find our way home.

When we are rooted in ourselves, in a healthy relationship with a healthy partner, intimacy becomes a kind of nutrition. It permeates and nourishes our cells, every fiber of our being. We are simultaneously seen and loved; we simultaneously see and love. We are willing to leave the relationship if we must, if it turns against our core values and damages our roots. But short of cutting off our own trunk, we do whatever we can to make it work.

Our ability to root in ourselves happens in stages, as does our ability to be intimate. As we root in ourselves we pass through doorways of unflattering mirrors that beckon to us, calling us ever deeper into our heart. This is a painful process, but we can be patient with ourselves. We can allow our intimacy skills to grow at an organic speed, to deepen as we age. We can allow these unflattering mirrors, these gateways of truth, to lead us home.

THIS MIRROR IS A LIAR! SELF-CONFRONTATION

There are many different ways to define success. Some of us define our success as the degree to which we have faced our inner demons.

To survive as children, we all suppress a specific part of our psyche. But, we do not all suppress the same part in the same way, so each of us has our own psychological patterns that can be quite distinct. The part that we do suppress becomes a kind of "back-ground operating system" in our lives, running in our brains without conscious awareness. This is what Carl Jung referred to as "shadow", our deep and distinctive paradigm that runs our emotions but only exists on the periphery of our awareness. This shadow also reflects the "rules" that we *expect* others to follow, as if *our* private emotional rules applied to the rest of the world. This shadow is the part of ourselves that we

The only devils in the world are those running around in our own hearts. That is where the battle must be fought.

MAHATMA GANDHI

A man with outward courage dares to die, one with inward courage dares to live.

LAO-TZU

confront while looking in the mirror, the part that we instinctively try to avoid. Courage involves facing our fears in facing the *enemy*, but what if the enemy *is us*? *Then* what does courage mean?

In relationships, our partner becomes the sacred reflection of our shadow. In order to create our own root system we must look to that reflection. We cannot create a root system without self-confrontation.

Of course the person we choose to hold that mirror can be of supreme importance. While anyone we meet can be a mirror, we may not want to *move in* with just anyone. Again, we should choose our partner well. When we choose our partner we enter a room full of mirrors. We can look into those mirrors… or not. Sometimes we look, and sometimes we do not. When we look, we do so by reclaiming our balls. Sometimes we do not look into those mirrors; instead we avert our gaze. When we avert our gaze, we do it by telling ourselves *stories*.

STORIES

In order to avoid looking in the mirror we tell ourselves *stories*. Our stories are revealed in our self-talk and what we tell others about our situation. We use our stories to avoid pain and discomfort, the very same pain and discomfort that point us toward our healing. We use our stories to avoid accountability for our lives and our behavior. We use our stories to avoid growing up.

We tell ourselves all kinds of stories:

We may believe that we are victims. (*And so we continue to victimize ourselves and those around us*)

We may tell ourselves that she is a *slut*. (*There are no sluts, only women who occasionally act like men*)

We may believe that we cannot change our behavior. (*How convenient*)

We may say that our parents made us this way. (*That may have been true until we were eighteen years old. But what was our part in it? And how many years have passed since we were eighteen?*)

We have not passed that subtle line between childhood and adulthood until we move from the passive voice to the active voice - that is, until we have stopped saying 'It got lost', and say, 'I lost it.'

SYDNEY J. HARRIS

Women might be able to fake orgasms. But men can fake whole relationships.

SHARON STONE

We may believe that we are unlovable. (*And so refuse to be kind to ourselves and others*)

We may believe that we make bad choices in partners. (*That may be true, but could it also be true that we behave badly?*)

Slowly, life takes our stories apart, brick by brick. And, if we are fortunate, the whole building eventually collapses. We yearn to be respected without acting respectably, honored without acting honorably, and loved without being lovable. Our stories create our inner myths that allow us to avoid accountability to our Inner Grown-up.

THE INNER GROWN-UP: SCREWING OUR DICKS ON TIGHTER

When we really face our mirror and look inside ourselves without flinching, then we fully embrace our "Inner Grown-up". An important result of connecting with our Inner Grown-up is our acquisition of accountability and credibility. This means that if we are to be credible, we must align what we say with what we do. This means keeping our commitments, even when it is not convenient. If we are fathers, we must be empathic enough to understand the impact that our behavior may have on our children. This means doing the right thing even when we are in pain or things had not turned out as we had hoped. This means doing the right thing even when we don't want to. It means screwing our dicks on tighter.

To screw our dicks on tighter is to become accountable, to look in that mirror when we do not want to. To screw our dicks on tighter does *not* mean to *suck it up* or to *suffer in silence*. It means to have the courage to open up our chest and feel our pain while still controlling our behavior.

When we open to our pain without indulging in it, we center in ourselves and grow roots into the earth. This growth of roots, this self-centering, is also an form of self-soothing. The growth of roots becomes our way of supporting ourselves. We can expect general support from our partner *at some point,* but not necessarily while she is in reaction. Our partner is least likely to be able to give us support when things are at their worst. It is at times like this we must generate our own support for ourselves; we must self-center.

Our self-centering is not about repressing feelings or being distracted, it's about stabilizing our emotions and our behavior while still dealing with the tasks at hand. To a certain degree we can actively change our physiology and frame of mind. We can soothe ourselves, we can center ourselves, and we should teach this to our sons. Ultimately it is our own trunk and roots that must hold us up, not our partner's behavior.

Sometimes the support we think we need is really just a balm to keep us from looking at our inadequacies. Our partner's support cannot shield us from our own built-in insecurities, jealousy, and pain. We may react strongly to something or expect very high standards from our partner. Are we expecting to be coddled and justifying it by saying that we have high standards? Only after honest self-reflection can we differentiate between trying to maintain our core values and indulging in our avoidance of pain.

Sometimes the support we think we need is a balm to keep us from feeling guilt. But our partner cannot keep us from feeling guilt, only we can do that.

BAD DOG! BAD DOG! BAD DOG!

For many of us growing up, guilt was a food group. We had our vegetables, our meat, our grains, and our guilt. And we knew that we had to eat everything on our plate.

No one can beat us up as badly as the guy in the mirror. Remorse and regret are inevitable, given that we are human, but guilt is toxic and useless. We make mistakes, we regret them, and hopefully learn our lessons. But guilt impugns our *soul* and has nothing to do with self-confrontation. Sometimes guilt is used as way to *avoid* self-confrontation. If we are guilty, contrite, and *just feel bad enough,* then

*To sit alone with my conscience
will be judgment enough for me.*

CHARLES WILLIAM STUBBS

we have paid off some invisible God. We have been absolved of our "sins" and so are free to do the exact same thing all over again. We are *absolved* so we do not have to actually do the hard work involved in changing our behavior. Guilt can be our way of avoiding accountability.

Sometimes our guilt is also a reflection of a twisted arrogance. Deep down inside we feel that we are so powerful that something we do may destroy the inner terrain of someone we love, that they are somehow powerless in our relationship. While of course our choices have an *effect* on those around us, when we take on responsibility for someone else's feelings we deny them the power to make their *own* choices. Our guilt, in essence, can disempower others.

Similarly our partner may use our own guilt to manipulate us and to avoid the responsibility for *her* choices. When she does this she gives us imaginary power over her and abdicates her *own* power. When our partner abdicates her power she also conveniently abdicates her personal responsibility. Personal responsibility is often the *last* thing we want in our lives.

When someone is guilting us, we need to be aware of exactly what is happening. It can be a long struggle to see through manipulation and be rooted enough to avoid being hooked by guilt. One of the best ways to respond to someone who is attempting to guilt us is simply to "call" the behavior, i.e. point out what is going on. This can be in the form of humor *"Hey honey, are you serving vegetables with that guilt, or is it a-la-carte?"* Or it can be direct, *"Are you trying to make me feel guilty?"* The guilter will often then deny that they are guilting us. If we are sure that is what happening, a simple response to their denial might be *"I don't believe you"*.

Sometimes we feel guilty with no help from anyone else, and we will feel guilty even when others are not being manipulative. Some of us automatically feel guilty, no matter what happens. In order to distinguish between our shadow and others' manipulation we must know our partners and ourselves well. Our sense of rootedness can help in these situations.

And if *we* use guilt as a weapon against our partner or our children, the toxicity of that guilt will resonate throughout our relationships. Why is a grown man acting like a child? We can grow up. We can show who we are and say what we want. We may get what we want, or we may not, but at least our testicles will remain where they are.

Our Freedom Lives between Stimulus and Response

As mentioned previously the only thing in this world that we can ever *really* control is our own behavior. We cannot always control our feelings, and we sure as hell cannot control *other* people's behavior, much as we might try. We cannot always control what happens to us, but we can control how we *respond* to what happens to us. This gap, between what happens and our response to it, reflects how much freedom we have in our lives. If we cannot control our behavior, we are tossed about like a cork in a storm and other people can manipulate us. We need to spend as much time as we can in the gap between stimulus and response. The deeper our roots grow, the greater the gap that we can embrace; and the greater the gap, the greater our freedom. This process gives us the best opportunity we can have to become the man we want to be.

Becoming the Man We Want to Be

This book is about becoming the man we have always wanted to be. It is not just about how we show up in relationship, but how we show up in our lives. What kind of man do we want to be? What kind of men do we want our sons to be? And why should we look in that damned mirror anyway? It is certainly easier not to.

The reason we should look to that mirror is that we cannot be complete when pieces of us are in shadow. We cannot become whole when we have left important pieces of ourselves in the basement. We are only whole to the degree that we can completely shed light on all of who we are. Our disowned pieces can be found in that mirror.

Between stimulus and response,
there is a space. In that space is
our power to choose our response.
In our response lies our growth
and our freedom.

VICTOR FRANKL

The word integrity implies a state of *integration*, one in which our psyche and our soul is no longer compartmentalized. When we are in integrity our right hand does not ignore what our left hand is doing. If we are to come home, our right hand *cannot* ignore what our left hand is doing. If we are to reclaim our disowned pieces, we must integrate them; we must welcome them back home.

Integrity is not about perfection. Integrity is honoring our imperfections, knowing our limits, and working with what we have. Integrity is what used to be called *character*. Integrity is about aligning our words with our actions and our actions with our values.

Given that none of us are perfect, we all fall short of this goal. But perfection is not the essence of integrity. The essence of integrity is the process of holding ourselves accountable. We do not have to be perfect; we just have to be willing to *look*. The person we most need to be accountable to is the guy in the mirror. Our most profound lapses are when we are not accountable to ourselves, when our internal integrity is askew.

But when our integrity is aligned, and when we are accountable, we then have the opportunity to come into our power.

Neither Assholes nor Weenies: Coming Into Our Power

Somewhere within us is a healthy man, neither an asshole nor a weenie. In many ways keeping our balls means navigating between these two indulgences. A warrior without principles is a bully… an asshole. A man without balls is a weenie. Having balls has nothing to do with being macho or outwardly aggressive, it has to do with our ability to hold space and self-confront. There are many men who are genuinely gentle but are completely self-honest and self-confronting. They are not outwardly aggressive, nor do they need to be. Not all men should be physically or psychologically aggressive, except concerning principle. Men whose nature is to be aggressive and physical should be, as long as they maintain their integrity. We need sane aggressive men... to protect us from insane aggressive men. But gentle men can be warriors, and their importance should not be underestimated. Would Albert Einstein have lived a better life if he had gotten into fistfights? Would Bill Gates be a better man if he pumped iron like Sylvester Stallone? I personally know many kind men who face themselves ruthlessly and have much more of the warrior in them than do most macho dim bulbs. These men have not given away their balls. They do not fight physically, nor do they need to, as they are not involved in combat. They are good, decent, caring men and wonderful fathers. God knows, we could use *more* of them in the world. We need all *kinds* of men in this world if we are to survive.

*Supreme excellence consists in breaking
the enemy's resistance without fighting.
Thus the highest form of generalship
is to balk the enemy's plans.*

SUN TZU

Other Men

Navigating Assholes by Perceiving Their Vulnerability

There are a lot of males out there testing boundaries and, like Don Quixote, spend their time attacking windmills. We can find them in any schoolyard or demon-haunted bar. These males can be very intimidating, but their own aggression usually comes from a place of deep fear and inadequacy. Men that are "decked out" to look scary and intimidating often do so because they themselves are frightened and use their appearance to ward off any potential attack. The irony is that looking intimidating may ward off some types of attacks but it may invite others.

In any event, when we are in reaction to someone who is aggressive toward us, that person can then "run" us with his behavior; he can manipulate us to react in a certain way. He can control us by "hooking" us. One of the best ways to interact with an asshole without buying into their script is to consciously perceive their behavior as a result of a deep insecurity, and to *see* that insecurity as it manifests through their behavior. Have you ever had a man try to insult you and it had absolutely no effect, because you could see how *lame* he was? Macho is just insecurity with a bad paint job. If we perceive someone's arrogance or obnoxious behavior as reflection of how damaged he is, it is much easier to not react to him. Seeing him as lame, *but still possibly dangerous* (and without showing him any outward signs of distain) can "unhook" us. We still watch for signs of escalation, but we don't need to take the bait. We don't have to read from the script that he is handing us. When we are not reading from his script, when we are not in reaction, the gap between stimulus and response widens. We have options. Of course, we can choose to respond with violence, but usually, if we are paying attention, it won't be necessary. He may expect us to respond from fear or anger, but we can respond differently, in *spite of* fear or anger. If we read a different script, the asshole often won't know what to do.

Transforming Our Trauma

Other males have psychologically and physiologically traumatized us. Our brothers have betrayed us. Those we have counted on for support have vented their rage, projections, and pain upon our bodies, and we have done the same to them. The traumas we have experienced are real and they linger in our nervous systems. The repercussions of this betrayal on our psychological imprinting cannot be underestimated. Much of our rage in the world is the direct result of this betrayal.

When we are traumatized our bodies internalize the experience as a somatic memory. The trauma is turned into a neurological pattern, a pathway that has a propensity to repeat itself. These traumas are lodged in our nervous system as shadow, as neurological tape-loops. They repeat themselves endlessly through the subtle nuances of our daily interactions with other men… and with women. Our patterns of trauma inhibit us, freeze us, and imprison us in ways so subtle that we do not even consciously perceive their impact.

Human trauma is somatically induced and it can be somatically

Nearly all men can stand adversity,
but if you want to test a man's
character, give him power.

ABRAHAM LINCOLN

released. The ways to do this are beyond the scope of this book, but there are many wonderful people who do this work. They are training others, often in high adrenaline states, to create a sanctuary within themselves that allows them to integrate and transcend past traumas. For more information see *Resources* on page 251.

COCKS, ROOSTERS, AND THE PECKING ORDER

In days of yore we were tribal creatures, and in our behavior we still are. Generally speaking, a tribe is a group of less than 150 members. Each tribe has an internal "pecking order", one language, one religion, and a single paradigm. The male portions of these tribes were held together by a *vertical* pecking order. Male pecking orders are more vertical than women's. We men will often align ourselves with whatever pecking order is placed in front of us.

In our genes and deep paradigms we are still tribal, but hunter-gatherers no longer roam the planet. In spite of our advanced technological lifestyle, we still re-create tribal patterns in our lives. So which tribe and pecking order are we in? That depends on the situation. On any given day, we men may pass through 4 or 5 different and distinct pecking orders and find ourselves positioned differently in each one. At work, on the golf course, at the playground, or at the dojo, each situation may well have a different hierarchy with different rules and values. So our place in the pecking order can be relative and somewhat random. But no matter what rung we stand on in this random hierarchy, it does not reflect our value as men. It does not matter what others think of us, or what the social mirror reflects, if we are rooted in ourselves then we know who we are. Our strengths and weaknesses remain the same. This doesn't mean that we ignore the pecking order or ignore reasonable boundaries. They are important. It's always possible to acknowledge authority without giving away our power. We just don't mistake temporary social status for significant personal power.

There are a number of mechanical devices that increase sexual arousal, particularly in women. Chief among them is the Mercedes-Benz convertible.

P. J. O'ROURKE

Yes, it's true that women tend to like men who are higher in the pecking order, but the question is *which* pecking order. There are lots of pecking orders floating around these days. So, we can find a pecking order in which we can rise to the top. We can become the head biker, the winner of the spelling bee, the world's best donut maker… whatever. We just need to remember that our rung on that ladder is no substitute for self-esteem, and that bragging will never elevate our status.

Letting the Qi Out

In our drive to climb to the top of this imaginary pecking order we might be inclined to "crow" a bit. Our inner rooster may really want to let loose and just brag. Yes we *are* the champion donut maker! Unfortunately, if you think about it, bragging never really works. Have *you* ever been impressed with a braggart? The Chinese believe that if we have a skill or a certain amount of knowledge, that gives us a certain amount of "Qi" or energy. If we brag to others about what we know, own, or can do; then they say that we have "let the Qi out", meaning that we no longer have it inside. When we have let the Qi out, we have lost the original energy of our accomplishment. It is no longer ours.

When we brag, we *run away* from our roots, we cut ourselves off at the knees. In bragging we try to convince ourselves, through the eyes of others, that we have value. We may indeed have value, but we will never know it because we do not bother to search inside to see what that value might be. We furtively hope that we can somehow absorb our value vicariously through the perception of others. Of course, this is always the paradox in trying to impress others. The only women we can impress by showing off are women who are impressed by show offs. This is similar to the dilemma of using money to attract women. Money may attract women, but it will only attract the women who are attracted to money. Then what?

Selecting a Goddess

Selecting (Recognizing) our Partner

At some point we will feel ready to create partnership in our lives. When meeting a potential candidate there are questions we should ask ourselves. Does our potential partner resonate with us? Does she resonate more than just sexually? Is there a deeper connection? Do we like how she shows up? Does she align with our values? And more importantly does she align with our *core* values? Core values are values that are non-negotiable. Core values are those values that, if compromised, preclude us from continuing our relationship.

Is our potential partner rooted in herself? Some ways to tell might be: She listens carefully and does not seem overly concerned with "fixing" our emotions. She allows us our process without getting into reaction. She voices opinions without necessarily feeling a need to defend them or needing consensus. She feels no need to brag or to show off. She shows integrity in her daily affairs. She expresses anger without slinging blame or guilt. She makes clear requests. She is accountable. She allows herself to be wrong. She self-discloses in an appropriate way. She is empathic without being ingratiating. She is

No change of circumstances can repair a defect of character.

RALPH WALDO EMERSON

When a man steals your wife, there is no better revenge than to let him keep her.

LUCIEN GUITRY

sensitive to our needs without fawning. She is strong without being demanding. She sets boundaries without being hypercritical.

Now we can re-read the previous paragraph and turn the mirror back on us: Are *we* the kind of person we would want to have as a partner?

Our potential partner will always tell us ahead of time how she will treat us in the future—we just have to *listen*. Is she still friends with her former partners, or does she speak of them with *contempt*? Does she confess their sins and speak of how *horrible* they were; conveniently neglecting to mention that she *chose* them, and that she was responsible for fifty percent of those relationships? Is she perpetually the victim? Does she flirt and then feel contempt for men when they respond? Does she always need to be rescued? Is she cheating on someone *with you*? Does she tell how she *got back* at her landlord? How does she treat women that she doesn't like? How does she treat people that she doesn't need? Is there anyone she *hates*? Have you caught her lying? Can she be purchased? If so, what would be the cost? How does she act when she doesn't know what to do? Is she accountable? What is her relationship with her family, particularly her father and mother? Where and how is she likely to not show up, to *not* look into her mirror?

Remember also that women's perceptions of their former partners can be remarkably self-serving and one-sided. Before we get all pumped up in some self-righteous huff about that *other* asshole, we should remember that some women play men off against each other because they like to watch the sparks fly. It can make them feel *desired* as they watch those men *jousting* for them.

When we first meet our potential partner, we may be smitten. You know the feeling—our glands swell, our heart pounds, our eyes glaze over, and our brain switches off as blood is shunted to more urgent parts of our anatomy. Regardless of our hormonal or cardio-vascular challenges, this is the time we should pay *close* attention to our potential mate. This is when we gather information about how she is put together. We compare values, feelings, and compatibilities.

Most importantly we watch and listen. We ask questions. We listen to answers. What do those answers mean? We extract *possible* meanings from the information, but we wait until we have had more time before drawing conclusions. We gather information but we do not make snap judgments. Red flags are noted and filed. If appropriate, we ask for clarification. This process may seem somewhat impersonal, but it's a sane counterpoint to infatuation, hormonal obsession, and the danger of a carnival mirror. Consider how many relationships we have had in the past in which we've ignored important signals from our partner. We need not judge her; we are just seeing if we are compatible. There are thousands of spectacular and well-differentiated women out there who would make terrific mates, but not for us.

Sexual compatibility does not a relationship make. It is only one vote out of many. Well, maybe more than *one* vote, maybe *two or three*. But it should not stuff the ballot box, rushing us into commitment. Depending on how high sexual compatibility is on our values list, we can navigate accordingly.

RUSH TO RELATIONSHIP

Many of us *over-commit* at the beginning of a relationship. Sometimes we are so desperate to get into a bed or a relationship or a marriage that we talk ourselves into things, things that are not based on reality.

Some of us will lie to a woman in order to get what we want, but this is not what we are discussing here. Lying to a woman, including lies of omission, in order to get laid is so far down the evolutionary ladder that it makes slime mold seem appetizing.

For the rest of us with at least minimal aspirations to integrity, in our blinding glandular rush to bond with another *we often only see what we wish to see*.

We may believe what our potential partner tells us rather than understanding that she can only tell us what she knows *at that time*. Like us, she may not have herself completely figured out. She may

The triumph of hope over experience.

SAMUEL JOHNSON ON SECOND MARRIAGES

Painted cakes do not satisfy hunger.

honestly believe that she is equipped to handle situations that in reality she is not. And we may think that we are ready to handle things for which we are not really prepared.

Seeing our woman as she really is and not as we, and she, would *wish* her to be is obviously very important. It becomes even more important if there are children involved in the relationship. If we are involved with a woman we are almost always involved with her children to one degree or another, and she with ours. If we misunderstand the person to whom we are about to commit, we risk not only our relationship with her, but we also put the children at risk as collateral damage should things fall apart.

If we are Internet dating the situation becomes even more treacherous. Geographical distance, pounding hearts, and swollen reproductive glands can make perilous bedfellows. We may think that the only way to really get to know our potential beloved is to move, either she or us, including career, family, home, etc. While this may be true, it also puts us at risk for losing much more than a potential relationship if we are hasty. This situation becomes even more convoluted and difficult to navigate as we get older, acquire property, and begin to have families. If we are far from our potential partner we may have some difficult choices to make that involve more than just ourselves individually.

There is only one unpleasant and necessary solution for all of this. *Time.*

In our rush to partner with our potential beloved we may overlook the importance of getting to know her over time. We will need to see things over time, good and bad, as they rise and fall over months and years.

OUR INFLATABLE GODDESS

From the time we are born, men and women are inundated with inflatable anti-gravity fantasy images of what our bodies ought to look like if we are to be sexy. As young men, many of us entered puberty via the portals of Playboy, Penthouse, and Hustler magazines. The objects of our lust and our subsequent expectations were completely unrealistic. Today many young men enter puberty through the portal of Internet pornography. These distorted images of women and sexuality can easily skew young minds. Sexuality need not always be "sacred" but such things easily impact the mind of a young person.

Honestly, could anything be *less* representative of sacred sexuality than pornography? As adults, Internet pornography is not nearly as damaging to us as it might be to someone in the midst of puberty. It is easier for adults to differentiate pornography from reality. But for a young man to imprint Internet pornography as his primary sexual paradigm is a travesty, especially if he *believes that it represents reality*. It is a travesty not only for him, but also for any of his potential partners. It can thwart possibilities for deep intimacy later in his life. If we should ever aspire to become a really *bad* lover, all we need do is imitate what we see in pornographic videos.

Of course men are attracted to beautiful young women. Young women are often beautiful and, Nature, in all Her wisdom, has made sure that men are attracted to beautiful bodies of reproductive age. But this is a very one-dimensional situation.

We always seem to forget that no matter how gorgeous she is, somewhere, right now, there is a guy who is really glad that she is *not* in his life. If we mistake our illusions for reality we may become that guy, and learn his lessons the hard way. Just because she is beautiful, that doesn't mean that we should mistake our physical attraction for something *deep* or *meaningful*. We need to look deeper, longer, and harder before committing to a Siren's call. If we expect perfection in our lover's body, or in our own, then we are in for a world of hurt, frustration, and disappointment. We can easily cheat ourselves out of potential depth, deep eroticism, and profound partnership.

The media takes full advantage of our ability to self-dupe. Our own glandular inclinations are subverted and used against us. These media images hold tremendous power over us.

Through magazines, television, and the Internet, we allow people

My reactions to porno films are as follows:
After the first ten minutes, I want to go
home and screw. After the first twenty minutes,
I never want to screw again as long as I live.

ERICA JONG

*Future generations will look back on TV
as the lead in the water pipes that slowly
drove the Romans mad.*

KURT VONNEGUT

into the deepest and most vulnerable parts of our psyches that we would never dream of inviting into our homes. Young people's minds, both boys and girls, are imprinted and indoctrinated with impossible standards, standards that no human being could ever hope to achieve. That these cartoons hold such power over our self-esteem, particularly for women, but also for us as men is a collective tragedy.

Our society has taken the most sacred aspects of our partnering, our sexuality, and made a mockery of them. We cannot allow profit-driven corporations to define our bliss. Our Sacred Temple has been desecrated, but *we can take back our paradigms*. We take back our paradigms by consecrating our lives, by honorably worshipping our partners and becoming worthy of that worship in return. We take back our paradigms by insisting that our lives have *meaning*. We take back our paradigms by living our lives as works of art. We take back our paradigms by finding our balls, looking to our deepest values, and refusing to compromise. We take back our paradigms by showing our children how we love. We take back our paradigms by refusing to be seduced by temporary distractions or nutritionless encounters. This society has taken much of the nourishment out of our food; *we will not allow it to leech it out of our lovemaking. We will not allow our temple to be desecrated*.

We can find joy in our bodies in the way they carry us today. The truth is that we cannot know, nor can we judge, the pleasure of which someone else is capable by looking at his or her body. "Sexy" is different than "beautiful", and "beautiful" can mean a thousand different things.

Of course we want to look as good as we can and be as healthy as we are capable, but we need to use reasonable standards for ourselves. We are not, nor do we need to be, movie stars, with thousands of people chasing after us. We cannot allow these cartoon images to dilute the nourishment we experience from intimacy. *We need not come to our unions in shame*. We can join with our partners without regret. We can use our erotic energy as healing energy. We can be who we are, exploring bliss with a partner who experiences our body as the pure manifestation of our spirit.

SACRIFICING THE GOOD GIRLFRIEND

Some women have a *Good Girlfriend* or a *Good Wife* inside them.

Before a Goddess can be born this *Good Girlfriend* must be sacrificed. The *Good Girlfriend* believes that unless she is *sweet and ingratiating,* men will not be attracted to her, that she will not be loved. Sadly this is sometimes the case. But a man who is differentiated will know that a relationship with a woman who is not differentiated may be well nigh impossible… doomed from the start. Even a relationship between two people who have done their work can be perilous at best, but if either partner is not committed to self-confronting, the landmines are almost guaranteed to explode wherever they step.

The *Good Girlfriend* avoids her truth if she feels that it might be in conflict with what her partner wants. Desiring to please, she has not yet learned that the truth is always more important than our feelings about it. The *Good Girlfriend* puts our needs before her own and thus cannot afford to speak her deepest truths. As we might guess, her unspoken truths do not go away; they eventually find their way to the light of day. And when her unacknowledged truths finally emerge into the light, they will bite us in the ass.

If we want a deep and intimate relationship, we must not only accept, but also encourage our partner to embrace her *own* wrathful deity. Sorry guys, we cannot have Aphrodite without Kali. Nor would we want to. Without her deep and sometimes wrathful strength she will be unable to weather the storms inherent in a profound and intimate relationship. Encouraging her in her process does not mean giving up our balls. On the contrary, keeping our balls means we can stand in her fire without being burned. The light of her rage may illuminate our mirror, and we may not like

*Until you've lost your reputation you
never realize what a burden it was
and what freedom really is.*

MARGARET MITCHELL

I think she must have been very strictly brought up, she's so desperately anxious to do the wrong thing correctly.

HECTOR HUGH MUNRO

that. But if we are rooted in ourselves her fire will not burn us. We may even come to find it as a great gift. Her fire will illuminate our integrity… or lack of it.

When she is in process, we are supportive but we do not coddle her. We still hold her accountable to not sling rage and blame, but we can encourage her to explore the truth and validity of her pain, confusion and anger. The more we can hold space for her and not pressure her into reverting back to the *Good Girlfriend*, the more our partner will be capable of intimacy and communion. Of course this can be risky in the short term; we may hear things about ourselves that we don't want to hear. This can also be risky in the long term; she may come through the transformation not wanting to be with us, or asking us to make changes that we find unsettling. All we can do is be a willing witness and not turn our back on her, *especially* if she is telling us painful truths. If we are only capable of accepting and loving her as the *Good Girlfriend*, we will never find our balls.

We may also find that we want to fix her, but we must resist the temptation to try. We cannot. This is hers and hers alone. Our humility is the knowledge that we cannot fix this; she can only navigate this by herself.

In her transformation from *Good Girlfriend* to Goddess, she will go through her own confusion, rage, and grief, just as we do in our process. The *Good Girlfriend* will be uncomfortable owning the personal power that those emotions will trigger in her. But without this power she will be unable to root enough in herself to truly *meet* us; to *see and be seen by us*. Without this rooting she will hide from us the parts of herself that she thinks we do not want to see. In hiding herself from us, both heat and light will be generated, but trapped. The trapped heat will emerge another time, via shadow. By denying her truth she covers the lamp that illuminates her path.

So we must encourage and support her in her path without knowing the outcome. We may win or we may lose, but we must roll the dice.

If she chooses to uncover that lamp it will illuminate her path. Her pain will become a compass that points to her healing. Her flaws will become her salvation and the fire of her pain will anneal her. And if we are worthy, her fire may anneal us also. Just like us, our partner finds her divinity through her humanity.

*Women have a special corner of their hearts
for sins they have never committed.*

Cornelia Otis Skinner

*I am constantly astonished by the people,
otherwise intelligent, who think that anything
so complex and delicate as a marriage can be
left to take care of itself. One sees them fussing
about all sorts of lesser concerns, apparently
unaware that side by side with them —
often in the same bed — a human creature
is perishing from lack of affection,
of emotional malnutrition.*

ROBERTSON DAVIES

Preparing for a Relationship

A Relationship is a Path

I n many respects, a relationship is a "path" or "yoga", a path of *self-knowledge*. It is a *practice*, similar to other paths of self-knowledge such as meditation, prayer or martial arts. Like meditation, prayer, or martial arts, the final destination of the path of relationship is a place within us. The final destination is who we become by traveling this path. When well-traveled, these paths, these yogas, take us home to ourselves; they lead to our healing. *We* are the destination of our path. If our relationships constitute such a path, then it does not matter how many partners we have had or how long those relationships have lasted. At the end of the day, and at the end of our lives, the only thing that matters is the integrity, self-honesty, and discipline that we have brought to this practice, to our path. It is easy to feel like a "failure" because we haven't found our "soul mate" or "life partner". Are our past relationships failures? Perhaps they are, but not because we are no longer in them. They are only "failures" to the degree that we did not learn the lessons they offered us… to the degree that we did not look in the mirror and walk down our path with integrity.

A RELATIONSHIP IS A GARDEN PATH

A relationship is a system that two people create together. If one person changes the way they relate to that system, then the whole system changes. It takes two people to create a relationship, but only one to end it. Put another way, a relationship is a garden that needs two gardeners. With only one gardener it will die. We must pick the right gardener with whom to share our garden. Both gardeners must weed the garden on a regular basis, or it will be overrun. A relationship is not a static, closed, system; it is a living, dynamic one. Like any garden, it needs proper amounts of sunlight, nutrients, water, soil, and love. Things must be planted at the right time, in the right way, and in the right soil. When all these pieces are in place we may create abundance. The more we put into such a garden, the greater joy and benefit we can harvest from it, and the more nourishment we will have in our lives.

Whatever garden we choose to create with our partner is the environment in which we must live. There is no escape from this. It is so obvious that we often fail to see it, particularly when we ourselves have been wounded. Any wounding that we do to our partner in reaction to our pain will resonate throughout the relationship. Eventually, there are always consequences. Blame is salt in the soil of our garden. Contempt is scorched earth. We cannot defecate in our nest and expect our lives to smell like roses. Being kind to our partner while maintaining our integrity can be one of the best long-term investments we can make in our lives. Our partner will trigger our shadow, the part of ourselves that we don't want to face. This is guaranteed. We can deal with it now or we can deal with it later, but we cannot escape the terrain that we co-create in our relationship.

A RELATIONSHIP IS A CONTAINER

In Asia, when they want to wash potatoes, they take a bucket and fill it first with potatoes and then with water. They then take a stick, put it in the center of the bucket, and pull it up and down. The stick moves the potatoes and all the potatoes end up rolling and rubbing against each other. The result is that they polish each other as they become clean.

In relationship, we become like the potatoes in that bucket. We create friction with our partner and, if we are willing to be polished, that friction polishes our character.

A Committed Relationship is a Sacred Container

A committed relationship is sacred container. That sacred container has two kinds of material in it, gold and shit. When there is enough gold in the container we will put up with all kinds of shit. But if enough gold is taken out of the container, then what we are left with is just shit. The ratio of gold-to-shit is different for each man, and when the gold-to-shit ratio becomes intolerable, we leave the relationship.

If we look deeper into the shit, so to speak, we may notice that what we thought was shit may not be shit at all. On closer examination what we thought of as shit might actually turn out to be painful-gold. Painful-gold is shit that has the *opportunity* to become pleasurable-gold, but not necessarily in the moment. In the moment it is just painful. Just as the shit we use in our garden can yield flowers, so can the shit in our relationship. Ultimately what we have with our partner is a ratio of pleasurable-gold to painful-gold.

Just as in our garden, we need the right amount of shit (painful-gold) to make the garden flourish. In correct amounts the shit is composted and transmuted. But if there is too much shit in our garden we will burn the soil and destroy our creation. Ironically the shit that has destroyed one garden is sometimes the most valuable gold of all for the next garden.

Now, if we have had many years of a pleasurable-gold stored up with our partner, we may have the ability to transmute a lot of painful-gold before it burns our garden. We may be able to use the alchemical furnace of our relationship and our history to transform it into pleasurable-gold, to turn it into flowers. But if we do not have enough pleasurable-gold stored up we will not be able to suffer through the process, nor should we. Life gives us plenty of shit to deal with and opportunities for growth without us needing to be masochistic. We carry the seeds of our own healing within us wherever we go. They are not necessarily contained in one partner. The ultimate purpose of our relationship may be more for our healing than our happiness.

COMMITMENT

The sacred container of our relationship has limits; those limitations are what make it a container. The limitations of relationship are its greatest safety, its greatest asset, and its greatest danger. Until we deeply root in ourselves we may see the limitations in relationship as a trap. This is the cliché of marriage in our society: We believe that when we commit we limit ourselves, that we are "trapped". If we are not ready for genuine commitment then a relationship can indeed be a trap. Ultimately, the degree to which we can commit to our relationship is the degree to which we can commit to our own lives… but only if we are ready to be annealed. In that annealing, our relationship becomes a temple of mirrors that allow us the possibility to reclaim our disowned selves.

Commitment is tenacity; it is the mortar that holds our values in place. Without commitment nothing happens. True commitment is like soil in our garden; without it nothing can grow. A healthy masculinity is *defined* by commitment; without it we are incapable of embracing our masculine nature. Committing is not about gritting our teeth and suffering; it is about recognizing who we *are* and what is important to us. Commitment must arise from the inside; it cannot be worn like a piece of clothing. It cannot emerge from outside us, from shame or guilt. We see who we *are* not who we *wish* we were, and our commitment arises out of that core. When we

I found God in myself
and I loved her,
I loved her fiercely.

NTOZAKE SHANGE

It is easier to marry qualities
than it is to develop them in ourselves.

ROBERT BLY

commit, we are really committing to ourselves, to our principles and our deepest values.

Commitments need not only concern sexual or relationship issues. Our commitment to creating a happy and healthy childhood for our children can be profound. We can commit to being single, faithful, polyamorous, or honest. It is when we are incapable of commitment to *something* that we are in danger of betraying ourselves. When we align ourselves with our values we create credibility, and this credibility resonates through our relationships. The ability to commit is the ability to delay gratification, and the ability to delay gratification is one of the things that defines a healthy man.

BECOMING THE KIND OF PARTNER
WE WOULD WANT TO BE WITH

Many of us have our "dream partner", the ideal partner we yearn for. We can visualize her, fantasize about her, and read all sorts of books about finding our *soul mate*, or *how to score with chicks*.

Of course our "dream partner" is just that: a dream. The person we fantasize about cannot exist except as a fantasy. Real women are like us: complex, conflicted, and often confusing. Still, the *type* of person we fantasize about is significant. The qualities that our dream partner manifests can reflect our deepest values, *and* our deepest shadows.

What characteristics does our dream partner manifest? Which of those qualities are most important to us? Knowing what those qualities are, what does our desire for them say about us? How much of our dreaming is a reflection of our core values and how much is a reflection of the way we seek to avoid pain? In other words, we may wish for our partner to manifest certain qualities so we can avoid the discomfort of having to create them in ourselves. We may wish for our partner to have money so that we do not actually have to go out and earn it. We may wish for our partner to be creative so that we can experience creativity in our lives without having to take the risks involved in a creative endeavor.

We must take responsibility for the projection of our own idealized self onto the other person. We need to have the courage and discipline to develop our *own* qualities, those qualities that allow us the possibility of manifesting our dreams. We must take the responsibility of becoming the kind of person with whom we would want a relationship.

LOVE WITHOUT BLAME

In relationship we must learn how to love without blame.

To love without blame is to fight fair and express pain while still keeping the "long view". To love without blame is to take responsibility for our choices and our behavior. To love without blame is to grow up, plain and simple.

Why should we love without blame? Because whenever we blame in a relationship we are *actively* trying to avoid responsibility. If we cannot take responsibility for our choices and ourselves in relationship, then we will never be truly nourished by one. When we blame we give away our power, and our balls, to someone else.

Blame is a poisoned mirror that we must reject. We reject it when it is directed at us, and we reject our own desire to direct it at our partner. Unless we wish to destroy the things most precious to us we should put it aside.

When we retaliate with blame or placate under the pressure of blame we diminish our spirit and smother the shining light of our deepest integrity. In blame we revert to being children. But we are not children; we are men. We can feel anger, even rage, but we can still hold space. We can deny a request or a demand but still hold compassion. And if we cannot hold compassion we can at least hold our tongue. Doing the right thing is at the heart of being a warrior. We can still do the right thing, even when we hate doing the right thing. Every time we do the right thing, the roots in our soul deepen, and we *become* something of substance that we can pass on to our children or to those we love.

My religion is kindness.

HIS HOLINESS THE DALAI LAMA

When we are deeply disappointed,
that's when the real relationship actually begins.

CHOGYAM TRUNGPA, RINPOCHE

We must not succumb to the temptation to blame especially when our partner is being a bitch, slinging all kinds of shit and not looking in her *own* mirror. It is when she is acting in this very un-Goddess-like way that we are most likely to give our balls away. If we give in to the temptation to retaliate when she blames, or to placate her when she blames, we might as well just hand her our balls on a platter. Just because we have given her our heart does not mean that we must give away our balls. Our partner may fight from the gutter but we have too much respect for ourselves to go there with her.

How do we do this? How do we love without blame? We love without blame by looking in our mirror and communicating in a way that reflects our integrity. Just as learning a new martial art or dance style requires learning a new body language, so does learning a new relationship skill require us to learn a new emotional language. This will require us to phrase our feelings in unusual ways and learn to express who we are without being critical or demanding. The way we phrase things is a reflection of the assumptions that we bring to our relationships.

There are numerous systems of compassionate communication out there and they are all worth learning. At first, learning such a system may feel stilted... as if we are playing word games. But these are not just word games. The words that we use and the phrases with which we communicate reflect our inner terrain and reveal the assumptions from which we proceed in our relationships. Our phrasing can help us to habitually look into the mirror. It can have a profound influence on the quality of our relationships. As we change the way we phrase things, it can actually help us change the way we think. *Our language can help us to grow up and grow roots.*

Blame and guilt are two sides of the same coin. When our partner blames us she may be saying things about us that are *true*. This is where our integrity comes into play. We must check in with ourselves and be brutally honest. If what she is saying is true then we must self-confront and acknowledge it, at least to ourselves. If we can acknowledge this truth in front of our partner without succumbing to guilt or blame, so much the better. But if we cannot expose ourselves without plugging into her guilt loop, then we should make a mental note that she has nailed us in a very unloving way. And we must make a commitment to ourselves to address these issues so that we can become the man that we want to be.

But it is equally important that we reject the way she presents the information to us. This is crucial. Being *right* in a relationship is not enough. There are many other ways that she may have expressed her disapproval of us, the most obvious of which is to make a request for us to change our behavior. The very fact that she did not or could not express her displeasure without resorting to blame says something significant about her.

We can set strong boundaries without indulging in blame. As a matter of fact, strong boundaries are often best expressed in a quiet voice. Sometimes the louder we speak the less we are heard. We can express strong anger without blame, although if the anger is *too* large, we often will be better off walking away and coming back when we have cooled off a bit.

The degree to which we can be in relationship without dishing out or absorbing blame is a direct measure of how much we still have our balls. Our ability to keep our balls is often a measure of how resilient we are in handling our own emotional pain.

EMOTIONAL PAIN

Blame is always an expression of internal emotional pain. We will experience emotional pain in our relationship; we can count on it. Our partner *will* trigger our emotional pain… that is what partners do. But just because we are in pain does not mean that someone necessarily did something "wrong". This is a remarkably tricky situation. There are three possibilities in the scenario of our pain. The first is that our partner is acting in an inappropriate way given the context of our relationship and our previous agreements. In this case their inappropriate behavior is triggering our feelings of pain. The

*The purpose of life is to be defeated by
greater and greater things.*

RAINER MARIA RILKE

Knowledge speaks, but wisdom listens.

JIMI HENDRIX

second is that our partner is behaving in an appropriate way and that our pain is arising from our shadow. The third is a combination of these two: That our partner is behaving inappropriately *and* an issue within our shadow has been triggered. *No matter which of the above scenarios turns out to be true, we must forgo the temptation of trying to wound our partner when we are in pain.* This frequent retaliatory wounding is not forgotten and healed; we simply store it away to later emerge as muscle tension, digestive ulcers, psoriasis, or tumors. When there is conflict and the possibility of recrimination, we must sort out what is our shadow from what is our partner's. This can be difficult to do and takes some perspective, distance, maturity, and self-honesty. When we are hooked or in reaction, this is the wrong time to sort things out. We should go and cool off, returning later to try to make sense of what has happened.

And we should remember that every incidence of emotional pain that we experience is an invitation for us to move toward our healing.

Validating our Partner

Active listening is the process of listening to our partner with the intention of reflecting her feelings back to her. The idea of active listening is that when we reflect someone's feelings back to them, we may improve the quality of our relationship with that person.

Like compassionate communication, validating our partner's feelings can also seem like a word game. But validating is also the verbal equivalent of growing our own roots.

Validating our partner's feelings is always a good idea. Not mandatory, but a good idea. Notice that I said validating her *feelings.* We can validate her feelings without validating her behavior or agreeing with her judgments or perceptions. We do not need to validate her blaming or slinging shit or throwing things, but we may be able to validate the fact that she is angry.

Of course when *we* are in deep process and angry as hell, we are not likely to validate her, and that is fine. But if we can do it without making ourselves crazy, validating our partner's feelings can be a good investment in our future relationship. It can allow our partner to feel *heard,* and *too few people in long-term relationships feel truly heard by their partner.*

A second benefit to validating our partner is that when we validate her, especially when she is saying something that we do not want to hear, we also drive our own roots deeper into our soil. If we can separate her needs and feelings from our own, we may recognize that we each can have valid individual perspectives and biases. In validating our partner, we may be able to reclaim our foundation.

Let's say this again: When we validate her feelings we are not *agreeing* with what she says, we are simply *acknowledging* that she has her own perspective. Our perspective will often be different. In validating our partner we can simultaneously differentiate and validate ourselves.

Of course, *we cannot and should not expect our partner to validate our feelings.* That is our job. If she does, that is great. But ultimately we need to be validating our own feelings, not waiting for our partner to do it for us.

Prioritizing Relationship Values

If we plan on keeping our balls, we will need to know who we are. Knowing who we are means knowing our values, particularly our relationship values, and referring back to them often. Values are best organized in a hierarchy, not because we need to be rigid and dogmatic, but because when we can prioritize our values, it means that we have examined them in a significant way and considered them from multiple perspectives. *See Appendix 1 for more on relationship values.*

Do We Want It Wide or Do We Want It Deep?

How many women can we *handle?* How many do we *want* to handle? Some men claim that they can be involved with more than one part-

Bigamy (noun): A mistake in taste for which the wisdom of the future will adjudge a punishment called trigamy

AMBROSE BIERCE, THE DEVIL'S DICTIONARY

We women are so much more sensible.
When we tire of ourselves, we change the
way we do our hair or hire a new cook,
or decorate the house. I suppose a man could
do over his office, but he never thinks of
anything so simple. No, dear, a man has only
one escape from his old self — to see a different
self in the mirror of another woman's eyes.

LUCILLE WATSON

ner simultaneously and still create deep and genuine intimacy. As your narrator, I must confess that I have not found this to be true in my life. If I am in a committed relationship and I am simultaneously navigating or scoping out other potential lovers, it takes away from the depth I bring to my partner.

Of course, there are times when we don't *want* depth, commitment, and intimacy—and that is fine. I do not believe there is any moral superiority in choosing deep intimacy over casual sex, or anything in between. Whatever we create we get to live in. Sometimes we are ready for intimacy, and sometimes we are not. Sometimes we yearn for romantic commitment, and other times it's the *last* thing we want. It can depend on our personality, where we are in our lives, and who we find ourselves with. Some men are not capable of deep monogamy and intimacy, for whatever reason; and being monogamous would not serve them or their partners. Others need monogamy and would be crazy to try to be polygynous. At different times in our lives we may need different things. But one thing is certain: Whatever path we choose, our morality revolves around the integrity with which we walk that path. It is important to be honest with our partners and ourselves. It can take a lot of work and many years to figure out what works for us and what does not, but we still need the balls to tell the truth as much as we know it.

THE WHITE KNIGHT, THE TIN MAN, AND THE GOLDEN TONGUE

Many of us yearn to be the *White Knight*. The *White Knight*, in addition to being good looking, rich, and skilled in all things, is also a fantastic lover. In order to ascertain if we are really the *White Knight* in bed we must look to our partner. We know that we are a fantastic lover when our partner has orgasms. Lots of them… the more and stronger the better. The bigger and better the orgasms, the more the carnival mirror tells us that we are not like those *other* guys. *We* know what we're doing. We know that we are the *White Knight* in bed because women tell us that we are fantastic lovers. Of course this is also why women fake orgasms: to prevent our inner *White Knight* from looking in the mirror only to see the inner *Tin Man* staring back at him.

We like women who climax easily and frequently as they make the best carnival mirrors. There is nothing wrong with being a good lover; it's natural to want to stand up and crow when we please our partner. But when our self-esteem is dependant on our "cocksmanship" something unfortunate happens. In the process of wrapping our value as a man around the frequency and strength of a woman's orgasm, we take both the orgasm and the responsibility of it away from the woman. Of course orgasms are a great gift, but they are gifts that *we help our partner give to herself.* We can't really *give* her orgasms because they are not ours to give; they are hers. In our delusion, her orgasms become our dominion and our pride… *our territory.* Her sexuality becomes our domain, her body our proving ground. This is just another variation on the age-old theme of women as property.

We may fear that without an adequate "performance" our partner may leave us. While this may occasionally be true, it is not often the case. Orgasms may be important to her, but rarely are they as important to a woman as intimacy and general compatibility. Would *you* leave a great relationship in which you were deeply in love just because your partner was not quite as skilled as a previous lover? Our partner doesn't want a *stud*; she wants to feel fully met by a man who has the balls to look her in the eye and embrace her, and himself, in an intimate and authentic way.

However, if her lack of orgasm is a *symbol* to her of *our* lack of consideration, that is another issue entirely. Then the issue is not about orgasms; it is about her perception that we are self-centered.

Misogyny is Desperation Turned Inside Out

We resent women because we *need* them. We need women for sex, admiration, nurturing, companionship, reproduction and worship.

Now I know what I have been
faking all these years.

Goldie Hawn in *Private Benjamin*

*The big mistake that men make is that
when they have turned thirteen or fourteen
and all of a sudden they have reached puberty,
they believe that they like women.
Actually you are just horny. It does not
mean that you like women any more at
twenty-one than you did at ten.*

Jules Feiffer

But we *resent* needing them. And even when we don't get what we want from women we *still* need them. Our need can turn to desperation; we can't ignore them. With enough pain and self-deception, our desperation can turn into resentment and finally anger and rage. We hate women because deep inside we feel weak and vulnerable. Women remind us of our deep instability, the frightened little boy inside, the one who yearns to feel *safe* and *powerful* and *loved*. Until we have the balls to look in that mirror, we will always push that little boy away, and blame women for our shortcomings.

WHEN FAIRY TALES BECOME CARTOONS

When the *White Knight* meets the *Damsel in Distress* or the *Good Girlfriend*, all hell can break loose. It may not be pretty. When we pursue our two-dimensional fantasy images of what love "ought" to look like, we bury land mines in our castle. Living in a fairy tale, we are constantly maintaining interactions that keep us from expressing our authentic selves. We cannot afford to be seen, lest we be discovered to be "lacking". In our striving to be "good" partners we vainly attempt to hide who we are beneath our cartoon. We manipulate and avoid real intimacy in our exhausting pursuit of this ever-receding cartoon fantasy.

There is no room for actual humans in the idealized castles of our *Fairy Tales*, and no ability to *see and be seen*. When we put our partner up on a pedestal eventually she will come crashing back to Mother Earth. And so will we if we are foolish enough to climb up there. To "Worship the Goddess" is not to put her on a pedestal; it is to create the container in which her roots can drive deep into the ground of her being. It is to honor the deepest spark of her flawed humanity and to hold the space needed so that she, and we, can bring out our best. Our Goddesses are real women, and we are real men. We are not cartoons. When we walk the path of intimacy we embrace her flawed humanity, and ours.

*God gives men a brain and a penis but only
enough blood to run one at a time.*

ROBIN WILLIAMS

*Our biological drives are several million
years older than our intelligence.*

ARTHUR E. MORGAN

Embracing Our Goddess

WORSHIPPING AT THE YONI OF OUR CHOICE:
OEDIPUS LOVES HIS MOMMY

In species after species, females are coy and males are not. Indeed, males are so dim in their sexual discernment they may pursue things other than females. Among some kinds of frogs, mistaken homosexual courtship is so common that a 'release call' is used by males who find themselves in the clutches of another male to notify them that they are both wasting their time. Male snakes, for their part, have been known to spend a while with dead females before moving on to a live prospect. And male turkeys will avidly court a stuffed replica of a female turkey. In fact, a replica of a female turkey's head suspended fifteen inches from the ground will generally do the trick. The male circles the head, does its ritual displays, and then (confident, presumably, that its performance has been impressive) rises into the air and comes down in the proximity of the female's backside, which turns out not to exist.

ROBERT WRIGHT, *THE MORAL ANIMAL*

83

Yep... *that's us*... we males are creatures of remarkable discerning intelligence. I recall seeing a film clip of a male cane toad attempting to mate with a female cane toad that had been flattened by a car and had been sitting in the hot Australian sun, unattended, for quite some time. Yum.

From the vulva we emerge, and to the vulva we perpetually return. As men, we know the power that a vagina has over us. Sometimes the whole world seems to be our "yoniverse". When we are "on the prowl" to "get laid" the whole world is miraculously divided into only three categories of people:

1) Those that possibly might have sex with us.
2) Competition for those that possibly might have sex with us.
3) Irrelevant.

What can make us act more like blithering idiots than a woman? Many of us would sell our souls for ten minutes inside the right vagina. It's as if our penises run the show. That's why we name them; we just don't want a complete stranger making all our decisions for us. But the *real* question is "What would we do if we knew we could do anything and not get caught?" This is another way of saying "What kind of man do we want to see in the mirror?"

A lovely dear friend of mine was once having troubles in her relationships with men. She went to a teacher of hers, a Native American shaman and asked him for advice. He told her that whenever she encountered a man in public, she should visualize the man staring at her and masturbating. He told her that after she had done this for a while, she'd begin to understand men. At first she thought he'd gone mad, but she tried it and told me that it profoundly helped her to understand her social interactions.

*Probably no male human being is spared
the terrifying shock of threatened castration
at the sight of female genitals.*

Sigmund Freud

The Yoni & Vagina Dentata: The Best and the Scariest Place in the World

Throughout history men have adored and feared women's genitals. Many cultures have myths about women being castrated males who bleed from their wound once a month. One of the most common archetypes about women's vaginas is the "vagina dentata", the toothed vagina.

Ouch.

The word "mother" has the same root as the word "mouth". The word "labia" means "lips" which implies teeth. The word "yawn" has the same root as the word "yoni". In the Middle Ages, the gates of hell were likened to a vagina, and the Inquisition claimed that witches could grow fangs in their vaginas. Interesting....

There are some who say that our fear of women also emerges from a kind of "yoni envy", in the sense that we are jealous and in awe of women's ability to give life. This jealousy may run so deep that we have even managed to misname what emerges from our loins as we make love. We call our ejaculate "semen", which means "seed". This is foolish, of course. We men don't have seeds; *women* have seeds. We might *wish* that we had seeds but we don't. What we ejaculate is *pollen*.

The Yoni and Gorilla Dentata

Some believe that when we are involved with a beautiful woman that we are in danger, and not just from the woman. The archetypal danger of a beautiful woman implies that there is always an alpha male just round the corner who is going to beat the shit out of us and claim her for himself.

Of course a beautiful woman can always be a great danger, and not just because of a gorilla. This inherent danger may explain the name of the plant Bella Donna, which means simultaneously a beautiful woman and a deadly poison.

BOUNDARIES AND SEXUAL ABUSE ISSUES

So many women have been abused as children or assaulted it boggles the mind. As men, as a gender, we need to take responsibility for this. Even if we as individuals have not been part of any of this and have not technically been part of the *problem* we still need to be part of the solution. At least one out of six women will be sexually assaulted in her lifetime; almost half are under the age of 18. Many say that the real numbers are actually closer to one out of three.

Because so many of the women we love have been victims of abuse or assault, we need to understand what happens when our partner goes into a stress response due to a past trauma. This can be difficult to navigate but we need to learn how to do so if we are going to embrace women.

One of the best things we can do for ourselves and our partner is to get stated consent before we engage with her physically or breach any sort of touch boundary. Just because our partner has been intimate with us before does not mean that we can take that intimacy for granted in the future. This can be easily included as a part of any ritual we undertake and will help our partner to feel safe and clear.

A primary reason for doing this is important. We need to understand that *the absence of a "No" does not mean, "Yes"*. Women (like us) are sometimes conflicted about what they want and will not speak up even when they are not comfortable. They may allow us to do something that will later cause them (and ultimately us) regret. Because of this we must take the initiative and get verbal consent before passing through any real or imagined boundaries. If we ask them directly and wait for response there is much better opportunity for our partner to have clarity about what she wants. This is especially important if we intend to penetrate our partner in any way, but also might include moving or removing clothing or even where we touch.

If we are role-playing with our partner this may obviously be bypassed. But if we are not sure, we should clarify the situation to be safe.

So, we can say, May I unhook your bra? May I enter you with my finger? May I kiss your yoni? This will indicate to our partner that she is safe, honored and respected.

Women who have been abused or assaulted may need professional help and we can support them by encouraging them to seek out that help. Women who have been sexually traumatized can store that trauma in muscle memory.

From a Daoist perspective this trauma is held in the body's memory as a rift between the Hun Spirit, the ethereal body ruled by the liver and the Po Spirit, the corporeal spirit ruled by the lungs. During any perceived threat to survival in her past these two spirits can separate and "lock" a repeated pattern of neurological dissonance into the body. This can create a kind of PTSD (post traumatic stress disorder) that can easily be retriggered through the medium of touch but also through other stimuli.

What that means is that she may relive the trauma in ways that she or we may not be able to predict. Trauma can easily be reactivated by sexual activity or intimate bodywork such as Rivers of Love. This is a somatic response and not under her conscious control.

When she is touched, but especially during Rivers of Love, she may react in ways that we cannot understand. She may find us hideous or freeze up. She may find our genitals frightening or repulsive. She may unconsciously and physiologically respond to us as if we were an assailant. She may shut down sexually. It is important to know that in these situations she is in her own world and her responses may have nothing to do with us. She is in shock when this happens, like a deer in the headlights. She may not even know what she needs or what she is feeling. She may feel numb and have tunnel vision or unusual physical symptoms. The best thing to do if this happens is to simply hold her and hold space. We should not try to fix her or stop her pain. She simply needs to feel supported. If she wants to talk, we can listen to her. Women who have been assaulted or abused will

My problem is that I am both attracted
and repelled by the male organ.
DIANE KEATON IN MANHATTAN

often feel shame about what has happened in their past. They may actually feel responsible for it. She may feel unlovable and damaged. This is a good opportunity to aid in her healing process by holding space and reassuring her that she is loved, worthy and whole.

The trauma of sexual violation need not only show up in our partner while she is receiving bodywork or making love. It can and will show up in many unpredictable places in her life.

In some ways, when a woman is in relationship with a man, she is in relationship with *all* men. Women in our culture are run through a gauntlet of sexual harassment, unachievable beauty ideals, and empty role models. Women raised in sex-negative households are taught from a very young age that sex is something hideous and disgusting that they should save for the person they love most. They receive a barrage of conflicting signals regarding sex, power, motherhood, and femininity. In this process, a considerable amount of resentment, frustration, and rage toward men may be generated. What this means is that our partner may have incongruous feelings toward us as men, and toward our penis as a symbol of masculinity and sexuality. Particularly for women who have been assaulted or abused the penis can trigger visceral memories of shame, trauma and betrayal. They can have strong physical and emotional reactions to our genitals, even if they love us.

We are complex creatures and our partner needs to be held and loved in all of her complexity. We can help her navigate this dilemma by giving her permission to feel conflicted about us as men. We sometimes think that if we love someone then we cannot simultaneously hate or loathe him or her; but that is not true. We can simultaneously loathe and love. In the case of trauma or abuse it is not necessarily us, but our gender, that can trigger such strong reactions. One of the best things we can do when our partner is having a traumatic flashback is to hold space.

If we have discussed this with her ahead of time, and she is open to it, we may consider practicing Infinite Touch with her (see *Wei Wu Wei*). But if we do, we must be prepared to *really* hold space.

HOLDING SPACE

Men hold space. When we are at our best we hold space. To hold space in a ritual is to create sacred space. To hold space in the world is to set boundaries, guard the perimeter, and draw lines in the sand. To hold space as a healer is to create opportunity for someone else to increase his or her quality of life. To hold space for our partner is to listen without preparing a response in our mind. To hold space for ourselves is to look into the mirror.

We create sacred space by building a home, setting a boundary, participating in a marriage ritual, and making commitments. To hold space is to withhold our judgments and our need for immediate gratification. When we hold space we create possibilities for others that we love.

Without sacred space, we abandon the sacred in our lives. Without holding space in the world, we are not safe nor are those we love. Without healing space our lives stagnate. Without space in our relationships our ghosts control us.

Aside from self-confronting, the most valuable skill we can bring to our intimate relationship is the ability to hold space within that intimacy. Through holding space we allow our partner to feel "met" on multiple levels. The more internal freedom we have created for ourselves the more space we can hold.

If we want our partner to heal and be fulfilled, holding space for her can also nourish us. To sit in the garden of our relationship and admire as she blossoms can create deep wonder and awe.

When we hold space for our partner, we listen. We don't need to fix her; we don't even need to help her. We need to *listen*. We have a supportive demeanor and are emotionally available. We allow her to process her feelings without interfering with her flow of information. This gives her psychological air. This gives her a break from the insane rhythmic masculine pounding that can punctuate our stressful days.

When we hold space for another we learn to hold space for *ourselves*. This means loving ourselves without judgment while still

*Scientists now believe that the
primary biological function of breasts
is to make males stupid.*

DAVE BARRY

Desperation… it's the world's worst cologne.

SHEILA KELLEY

striving toward integration. This means being as kind and unwavering with ourselves as we can manage.

When we are incapable of holding space for ourselves in our relationships we collapse our core values and betray ourselves. When we do not hold space for ourselves out in the world, we collapse around women.

COLLAPSING AROUND WOMEN

Many of us will "collapse" our own space when we are near a beautiful woman. Our tendency is to fawn over her or to manipulate her, which just reveals how little we value what we may have to offer.

When we fawn we collapse our core; we betray and abandon ourselves. We don't have to be arrogant or cocky to experience ourselves as having value; we just have to be real. We can admire and be attracted to a beautiful woman without humping her leg.

HANUMAN: SHOWING WHO WE ARE AND ASKING FOR WHAT WE WANT

In Indian mythology there is a monkey God named Hanuman who is the servant of the Goddess Sita and the God Ram. In one story he is asked if he can prove his devotion to Sita and Ram, and in response he tears open his chest revealing the two deities standing inside his chest. This self-exposure is the acid test of our rooting. If we can show who we are, all of who we are, without shame or arrogance, then we have rooted in ourselves.

We may believe that expressing clear information and exposing our emotional body means that we are being demanding. Or that it makes us too vulnerable. Of course, expressing who we are and saying what we want is not a manipulation or a demand, just an expression of fact. We may think that if we ask for what we want, our partner will have no choice but to comply with our wishes. We forget that she can say no. We forget that we are simply not powerful enough to take away our partner's sovereignty, nor her liberty. If we say to our partner, "I want you to do this", she can always tell us to go to hell. Our saying to her "I want you to do this" is simply a fact… this is what we want. We may want it, but we may not get it.

Questions also arise:

"How can we ask for what we want when we don't know what that is?"

We need to learn, to pay attention.

"Can we discover what we want without knowing what we're feeling?"

No.

A further extension of showing who we are is *asking* for what we want. We can say, "This is what I want" as a statement and tell our partner what we want. But we can also make ourselves even more vulnerable and ask for what we want. And we can ask without shame or apologies. "Will you do this"?

For some of us, asking for something directly is even more risky than simply *stating* what we want. We may feel that making a request puts us "one down" and at risk for rejection. We feel exposed in a deeper way. We have exposed not only our want, but we also have to ask for it. Asking implies need. What if our partner sees not only who we really are, but also that we actually have wants and needs? What if she sees us the way we see ourselves… ashamed of our wants and needs? When we ask for what we want, we are not just showing who we are; we are extending ourselves. In order to be vulnerable, to ask for what we want, we might just have to screw our dicks on tighter, to find our roots.

Sometimes, rather than just saying what we want and risking rejection, we manipulate people to give us what we want. Rather than just taking responsibility and screwing in our own light bulbs, we try to manipulate others so that they turn the ladder while we hold the bulb. We may even convince them that it wasn't a need that we had, but rather something that we deserved. They owed it to us... it was an entitlement. This can be a deep and unconscious form of cowardice.

A request for change is always a request for a change of *behavior*. Asking our partner to not feel angry or jealous is unreasonable. Like us, she cannot always control what she feels, but she can be expected to control her behavior in spite of her feelings. And the same holds true for us. Controlling our behavior in spite of our feelings is the hallmark of a grown up, and hopefully our partner and we are both grown ups. When asking for a change of behavior, the more specific our request, the better. "Honey, I know you get mad at me when I leave my laundry on the floor, but would you please not throw my socks in the toilet?" Of course, much to our chagrin, she can always say no. Or she might say, "Sure and you can also do your own god-damned laundry". Or she may negotiate. "Of course I will stop doing that, honey, just as soon as you install the new washing machine that's been sitting in the garage for a month." Your move....

We can also create a consequence for the behavior. "If you don't stop throwing my socks in the toilet, I will squirt cheese whiz up my nose." Or, "I will call your mother." Whatever. The point is that we can make requests and set consequences as we see fit, and none of this has anything to do with blame or blackmail. There is a huge difference between "You are a slob" and "If you don't pick your socks up I will leave you".

Now, making clear requests and setting consequences can still be manipulative, i.e. not in line with our values. In other words we can blackmail by crying wolf; we can set major consequences for minor inconveniences. But if we are manipulative and not rooted in our values, any woman worth her salt will smell this manipulation. Eventually, our bluff will be called. When we set important consequences they have to come from a place deep within us.

Making a direct request does not make us "one down" but it certainly does put us at risk for rejection. When we make a clear request

If men knew what women laughed about,
they would never sleep with us.

ERICA JONG

of our partner, it also reinforces their autonomy. By asking for what we want, we recognize that they can deny our request if they so choose. Then what? When that happens, and of course at times it will, there are a number of things to be considered.

If the denied request is about something that is not a core issue or a core value, then we can decide how important it is in the grand scheme of things. Perhaps we can compromise or find another solution to create what we want. In any event, clear communication should be a "food group" in our lives.

If the denied request conflicts with one of our core values, we may have to determine if this relationship is worth continuing. Of course, in order to do this, we need to know what our core values are. If we are not rooted in ourselves, then we do not know which of our values are primary and non-negotiable. If we do not know our core values, then we cannot afford to be vulnerable. The process of sorting out our values can take a long time. And our values can change over time.

Of course, our partner is autonomous. She can move on and find another man. Or woman. Despite what the carnival mirror may tell us, we are just one option among many. So if we are to bring a dish to this banquet, we'd better make it complete and nourishing for *both* of us. That means not only an appropriate offering for the Goddess, but equally nourishing for us as well. Learning to navigate this is the task of a lifetime. We can be patient with ourselves.

When Our Partner is Wifed-Out

We can only be best friend to our partner to a limited extent. We cannot expect ourselves to be everything to our woman, nor can she be everything to us. Our partner needs women friends with whom she can share her inner feelings, just as we need our men friends. When we become the only close friend our partner has we set the relationship up for a crash. We cannot take the place of our partner's women friends. She needs the space to bond and share with her women friends that which only women can know and feel. And sometimes what they share with each other is Phallic Scorn.

Phallic Scorn: When our Partner becomes a Bitch Goddess

While our happiness is *linked* with our partner's happiness, our happiness is not *dependent* on hers. Occasionally, our partner may come down with an acute case of penis pity or *contempt*. Truth be known, her scorn may have nothing to do with us. Assuming that we have selected a partner who is at least as rooted as we are, she will still have bad days, just as we do. On her bad days she may be unwilling or unable to look in her own mirror, much less reflect our image accurately. A quick check inside ourselves should let us know if we have been inappropriate or if she is just having a bad day. Her problems are not always our problems. Has she made a clear request to which we have not agreed? Is she in a vulnerable place in her cycle? Is her digestion off? In any event, no matter how much she loves us, she may still become a wrathful deity, seeking any available opportunity to relieve us of our balls.

When this happens, our first priority is to not get into reaction. Yes, she may intentionally say things to provoke us. We may even hate her. Later, we can decide if we really want to be in relationship with someone who would say such hurtful things, or if we should find another partner. But for now, we should just take a deep breath, screw our dick on tighter, and walk away until we have calmed down. We can say, "I cannot talk about this right now". In any event: We need to refrain from retaliating.

Even though we don't retaliate, we still need to protect ourselves, especially if there is wounding. We can always close like a flower or go into our cave like a bear. Sometimes we choose to open, and other times, when we need to, we remain closed. When we are joyous, we remain open, and when we are threatened, we close down. This is a sign of our natural intelligence and not a spiritual or psychological flaw. To remain perpetually open or perpetually closed is self-abandonment. If

*You love and respect yourself so much that
you don't allow other people to disrespect you.
You put boundaries on their wounds,
not because you want to avoid them,
but because you don't allow that
poison to come to you.*

DON MIGUEL RUIZ

we remain open all the time we are not protected. If we remain closed all the time we are not nourished. The stronger we are in ourselves, the more we can remain open while we are in pain, but this is not a mandate. Only we know for sure when we are closing down to really protect ourselves and when we are closing down from avoidance.

After we have been criticized or our partner has expressed pain or disapproval we may be tempted to "fix" the situation by compromising one of our core values in order to keep her placated. We may make a concession to her that in reality amounts to self-betrayal. We will know this is the case by the sinking feeling we get in our stomach after making such a concession. This concession is a mistake and can reveal our tendency to want to do our partner's work for her; to keep her from having to do it herself. We may want to protect her from her pain, but we cannot. Her pain is her own and any attempt by us to take it on is ultimately disempowering for both of us.

Relationships involve a flow of energy and are predicated on that energetic balance. They depend on the balance of energy between our partner and us and also on our internal balance. A relationship is a verb, not a noun, and the energetic field of that relationship is always in flux.

Later, when the energy is less volatile, the situation will be less heated. We can then ask ourselves important questions like: What kind of relationship do I want to be in? Is she just in a mood, or is this the pattern of someone who cannot look into her own mirror? No matter what her process, it may not be about us, or at least there may be nothing we can do about it. If she cannot be in relationship without blaming, or our core needs are not being met, then we should consider choosing another partner.

SCOPING OUT ANOTHER WOMAN
AND BRINGING IT HOME

When we are in partnership we *will* be attracted to other women; we can count on it. If we aren't, we just might want to check our pulse.

Our attraction to other women means that our guy parts are working just fine. This attraction is normal, and does not imply a lack of love or commitment. There are usually all sorts of beautiful women we encounter in a public place on any given day. But what do we do with these attractions, how do we handle them?

Well, if we *obsess* about an attraction, it may be a red flag for our relationship. It may mean that one or more of our needs are not being met with our partner and that we should pay more attention to what is happening in our relationship. We should check in and see if we have core needs that are not being met. If so, can we talk to our partner about those needs? Can they be met outside of the relationship without compromising our integrity?

But what if our attractions are sporadic and not obsessive? Well, we do not need to *act* on them unless we have a deep and abiding desire to invite Eris, the Greek Goddess of chaos and discord, into our lives.

Besides just limping around beautiful women, one of the things we can do is we can use those attractions as "food" for our relationship, for our commitment to our partner. Those attractions can be "recycled" back into our attraction to our own partner; we can take the juice that we feel from our attractions, bring it home and claim our partner.

STRENGTH, CAVE MEN, AND CLAIMING OUR PARTNER

Sex is intimately connected with aggression in human beings. This is the result of one million years of natural selection. Sex is also intimately connected with tenderness and kindness in human beings, another million-year-old inheritance. These two polarities are here to stay in us, at least in the foreseeable future.

Some of this polarity gets played out in our sexual dynamics. We may find power imbalances sexy. When we are dominant or submissive in bed, this can heighten sexual tension and excitement. This does not mean that we truly wish to be dominated, or dominate, outside of the bedroom. People with rape fantasies do not want to be raped. No matter how masochistic, unusual, sadistic, or fundamentally depraved

Men may love women, but they are in a rage with them, too. I believe that it is a triumph of the human psyche that out of this contradiction, a new form of emotion emerges, one so human that it is unknown to animals even one step lower in the evolutionary scale: passion.

NANCY FRIDAY

our fantasy may appear; it is just that... a fantasy. It only becomes a problem if our behavior in the world becomes inappropriate or coercive. These sexual fantasies are the reflection of the shadow realm of our psyche. In our humanity, we all have disowned parts of ourselves, and these parts will find always find a voice, somehow. Our fantasies are not bad, just the reflection of shadow. They display our humanness and the richness of our erotic terrain. We may feel that our own fantasies are shameful and quite possibly grounds for imprisonment in some medieval dungeon. But the truth is that no matter how bizarre, embarrassing, or depraved we believe our fantasies to be, they are not nearly as weird as our next-door neighbor's.

Deep down inside many women yearn to be *taken*. They yearn to be taken in spite of their cultural or political beliefs—and in spite of any shame that they might feel about it or any of our judgments.

If our partner wants to be taken, and it is within stretching distance of our comfort zone, we should *take* her. *We can allow ourselves to take her.*

Often, we will be uncomfortable really *taking* our partner. The threat of intimacy becomes too powerful; we feel as if we will lose our souls. We fear that if we *take* our partner we would lose the last shred of ourselves that was left. The only solution for this fear of intimacy is for us to leave the relationship or learn to become intimate. To learn how to be intimate is to become rooted in ourselves, to access the place inside us that *no one* can take away. Even if we have given our heart away, our balls and our integrity remain intact.

In *taking* our partner she must always know that we are playing. Anything beyond consensual play is inexcusable. She cannot allow herself to be completely taken until she feels completely safe. And we should never mistake this temporary "domination" as a diminishment of our partner's stature. Just because our partner wants to be dominated sexually doesn't mean that she wants us to act like an asshole. Women may want to be taken in their lovemaking, but few want to be treated as less than equals. Please remember, to fully "Worship the Goddess", we must be willing to fuck her like an animal, be as ingratiating and fawning as a groveling minion, or anything in between. The more flexibility we have in our lovemaking, the happier will be our communion. But whether we are sinking our teeth into her neck, gently sucking her toes, or giving her butterfly kisses, we control and direct our energy. We control and direct our energy no matter how aroused we are. Our antennae are always attuned to her as much as to our own pleasure. This can be counter-intuitive and it takes patience. As men in worship, our job is to hold space. Without holding space, we dissipate the energy and our relationship loses its container. This is the core of divine worship.

As a practitioner of traditional Chinese medicine, I have a patient who is 75 years old. She is a lovely, charming woman who has breast cancer. Recently I asked her "What is the *one* thing that is unfinished in your life?" She looked me in the eye and without missing a beat said "Wild sex with Roger!" The importance of *taking* and *being taken* should not be underestimated.

OFFERING OURSELVES UP

We keep our balls and hold space. We control and direct our energy. That's our job.

That is… until we don't.

We also need to be able to *lose* control. We need to allow ourselves to be fucked, to be at the mercy of our woman. Can we allow ourselves to be sacrificed on the altar of her lips? If not, why "Worship the Goddess" at all? We can allow her to take charge. We can lose control. We can *really* lose control. This is just as important as holding space. We can allow ourselves to be *fucked… to be taken.* Not enough skin to cover our eyes. Often our partner will want to see us out of control, out of our minds, just as we want to see her. What Goddess worth her salt does not want to occasionally milk her lover dry? To extract, to squeeze out our core life force for her own pleasure? Otherwise, why should she be a Goddess at all? To deny this to our partner could be a mistake, a lapse in judgment.

There is a little bit of vampire instinct in every woman.

THEDA BARA

There is nothing that impairs a man's sexual performance quicker than any suggestion that he's not doing it right.

HELEN LAWRENSON

On the other hand we occasionally may climax unexpectedly or fail to get an erection. Good. Keeps us humble. When we are humble we can admit that we do not know everything; we may yet have something to learn in this life about women and love. Humility can open the door to the great mystery. We can learn other ways of being sensual, and of being sexual. And in our new-found humility we may actually learn how to accept feedback.

ACCEPTING FEEDBACK

We men have a desperate need to look competent, which usually arises when we are not. This can occur either inside or outside the bedroom. As a gender we are generally not good at accepting feedback from our partner. This is especially true if she is giving us feedback about our lovemaking.

If we want to be a good lover we are going to have to face this. *There is no way we can please our partner without first finding out what pleases her.* We cannot become a good lover without discovering what that means to *each* woman. Yes, they are *all* different. Yes, it sucks, but we have to *ask*. It is like asking directions or reading the instruction manual. Get over it. We have to somehow generate enough humility to admit that we just do not know everything.

Each woman has different patterns, psychological terrains, and things that turn her on. As mentioned previously, we must tune our antennae to her; we *feel* her breathing, body language, muscle tension, and cues. But we must also ask her. We ask her what she likes. We ask her to show us. We can practice with her until we get it right with *her*. We can *learn how to learn*.

LEARNING TO LEARN: PATIENCE AND LEVELS OF COMPETENCE

The Rivers of Love techniques described later in this book, while ultimately fulfilling, can be challenging to learn and somewhat counter-intuitive for many of us. And when we are aroused it can be especially difficult to track breathing patterns and bodywork techniques. Tracking our breathing or thinking about our massage technique may be the *last* thing we want to do while making love. For this reason it is important that we have patience and take our time while learning the Rivers of Love material in the second half of this book. We should not try to learn everything at once. If something is difficult and frustrating for us, then we can take our time or relax into something else.

It has been said that there are four levels to achieving competence in any endeavor:

1) Unconscious Incompetence
2) Conscious Incompetence
3) Conscious Competence
4) Unconscious Competence

Unconscious Incompetence is when we are not aware that we do not have a skill. *We do not know that we do not know.*

Conscious Incompetence is when we begin to learn a skill but we are aware that we are not yet competent. *We know that we do not know.*

We become *Consciously Competent* when we have learned a skill but we must still think about it while doing it. *We know that we know.*

Finally, we become *Unconsciously Competent* when we have a skill and we can do it without even thinking about it. In martial arts this is also called Muscle Memory.

When we are first learning any Rivers of Love techniques it will be easier if we acquaint ourselves with them one at a time rather than trying to learn them all at once. We can focus on just the Qigong or just the bodywork, gaining comfort and familiarity with them slowly.

The Qigong breathing patterns like Small Heavenly Circuit we can practice alone until they become second nature. Once they have

*In theory, there is no difference
between theory and practice.
But in practice, there is.*

YOGI BERRA

A woman's most erogenous zone is her mind.

RAQUEL WELCH

been patterned into Muscle Memory, then we can begin to try them with a partner while just lying together, and then finally while making love.

We can practice the bodywork techniques on our partner or our friends without a sexual component. Although later in the book we mention that some bodywork techniques are only to be done in aroused states, this is only true if we are intending communion with our partner. We can certainly do much of this bodywork on our friends and family without involving sexuality. So we can practice Bone Washing on friends and even our partner until we feel comfortable with it. Finally, when we are comfortable, we can apply it to our lovemaking.

"Worshipping the Goddess" is not about performance; it is about communion. We can create blissful states with our partner simply by lying next to her and looking into her eyes. So we should not take the techniques described in the next section of this book and turn them into some kind of chore. When in doubt, we should default to spontaneous caring and intimacy.

In love, you pay as you leave.

MARK TWAIN

Losing a Goddess

Breaking Up: Losing a Goddess

Not every woman is for everyone. There are thousands of incredible men out there and an equal number of wonderful potential female partners, but they are not interchangeable. In other words, one wonderful woman who is perfect for a wonderful man may not be a match for another wonderful man. Neither one is better nor worse; they are just not matched. At some point we may need to end our relationship with our partner, or she with us. Perhaps we have changed, she has changed, or we just aren't as happy as we might be. But leaving or being left by a partner is no small matter and doing it well will test our integrity more than any other time in our relationship. It is also the time when the largest of our shadows may arise, and, if we are willing to gaze upon it, when the mirror becomes the least flattering. When we separate from our partner we should not need to take our balls back, we should not have lost track of them in the first place. If we have lost them; it is time to reclaim them.

The clarity needed to end a relationship exists on a continuum. We can always look back and say, "Damn! I should have left *sooner!*" or "Damn! I shouldn't have left *at all!*" It's a slippery slope of knowledge, and the answers that reveal themselves may be very different depending on where we are in our lives and the nature of our relationship.

In relationship, our damaged parts are most clearly revealed and exposed. When we lose a partner, those damaged and fragile parts are magnified as they float to the surface. How we react to that vulnerability is a measure of our courage.

We will always return to our pain, to the suppressed part of our psyche that wants to be whole. Our pain can be deep, almost unfathomable, but it will heal if we allow it. That pain is a compass that points to our healing, not only of our relationship, but also of our life. Any emotional pain at any time in our life is a potential portal into our healing. That needle on our compass of pain points toward our balls. We must accept the part we've played in breaking our own hearts, and understand how we may have led ourselves into crisis. Those women that have broken our hearts… if we let them, they can be our greatest teachers.

Yes, our hearts have been broken, but they have also been cracked open.

The Gift of Crisis: Cracking Open the Heart

When we return to our pain, to our shadow, we return to the dark parts of ourselves that we have not yet faced. We spend the first twenty years of our life creating shadow, and creating strategies to compensate for that shadow. And then, if we are somewhat lucky, and somewhat lucid, we spend the next sixty to eighty years *unraveling* what we have created. Over time, or if there is upheaval or trauma, our compensation strategies wear thin… they don't work as well as they used to. When those strategies can no longer keep our shadow hidden, a bright painful light may be shed upon them. This light can *hurt*. Then we are not only faced with an unpleasant sight, but

There is a love that begins in the head
and goes down to the heart, and grows slowly;
but it lasts 'till death, and it asks less than
it gives. There is another love, that blots
out wisdom, that is sweet with the sweetness
of life and bitter with the bitterness of death,
lasting for an hour, but it is worth having
lived a whole life for that hour.

RALPH IRON

*Our deepest fears are the dragons
that guard our deepest treasure.*

RAINER MARIA RILKE

we do not yet have any integrated, healthier strategies with which to replace the old ones. The shock of seeing our shadow emerging into light is called *crisis*. Properly handled, crisis can be the greatest gift we will ever receive.

When we are in crisis we have access to places in ourselves that, in happier times, are much more difficult to access. When we are in crisis, a *door* appears before us, inviting us to come through. That door is usually the *last* place we want to go. We may choose to walk through that door, or we may refuse. But the minute we locate our balls and we walk through that door, our healing begins… we are on our way home. The secret gift that crisis brings us is pain and *most of us only change when it's too painful not to.* The last thing any of us ever *really* want to do is change our behavior. But often it is this very change of behavior that brings us home to ourselves and nourishes the growth of our roots.

Yes, we have choices. We can take a good long painful look into that mirror, walk through that door and return home, or we can turn away from the door and put the mirror back in the drawer.

If we wait long enough, the pain of our crisis will diminish. And it will diminish whether we choose to walk through that door or not. The irony of our pain is that we have a window of time during which we must take that leap into the abyss of pain, into the unknown. The great tragedy is that if we choose to *not* walk through that door, it will close again. Then, we might have to wait another ten to fifteen years before we get another opportunity. We arguably only get four to five opportunities to create deep healing during our lifetime. Of course, the door doesn't go away. It's always there. It's just much harder access when we are not in pain.

The purpose of crisis is to crack open our heart. Our tears moisten our soil, allowing our roots to penetrate as we find our way home. It is in this way that our pain, and our partner, can each be a great gift to us. As our partner, and her loss, triggers our pain, she may have no intention of healing us. But that doesn't matter. We can accept our gifts in whatever form they appear.

Even when he was sad and exhausted he kept trying. Good fathers give us whatever they have.

SCOTT SIMON

Passing it on to Our Sons

On Being a Father

Ejaculating may make us a sire but it does not make us a father. Any dog on the street can ejaculate. The word "father" is as much a verb as a noun. To say that we are someone's father is only true if we *act* like a father. To be a father is to be an *anchor*.

Children are ten times more likely to be murdered by a man in the house who is not their biological father than by their biological father, much as young lions are killed by a new male who takes over the pride.

But we are not wild animals; we are not lions and we are not dogs on the street. The children under our care *are* our children, whether they are our biological children or not. Even if they are not our biological children, they are *someone's* biological children. Even if their biological father is a stray dog, we are not stray dogs. Our ability to appropriately and reasonably care for children is a measure of our character as men. And our caring and integrity can be passed on to our sons, possibly even allowing us to mentor their future.

PASSING IT ON TO OUR SONS: MENTORING THE FUTURE

When we self-confront without self-deprecating, we become worthy to embrace the Goddess.

When we self-confront without flinching, we become worthy to embrace our sons.

Our sons need to be nourished, cherished, and admired. They need to see their value in our eyes before they can generate that perception within themselves. They need to learn to feel their feelings and keep their chests open while staying strong. They count on us to find things in them of which we are proud. They need to feel our pride in them.

Our sons will not do what we *tell* them to do; they will do what we *do*. If we can show our sons that a sexual relationship between two people is an exchange, and that it has the possibility to be a sacred exchange, then they too will seek out and perpetuate this quality of exchange. If our sons see us self-confront, they will self-confront. If our sons see us honor our lives and our masculinity in a healthy way, they will honor their lives and their masculinity. If our sons are witness to our honoring and deep respect of women, then they too will honor women and treat them with respect. There are few choices in our lives that have the potential for such a deep and lasting impact upon our fragile planet.

PART TWO

Worshipping the Goddess

Healing energy and erotic energy are just different forms of the same thing.

DR. DEAN ORNISH

Rivers of Love: Sexuality in the Heart of Healing

While a lot of the Rivers of Love material takes place on a massage table, *none of this work should be construed as appropriate for medical or clinical use.* These techniques are designed for *couples in relationship only.*

A RIVERS OF LOVE APPROACH

Within our relationship, we should not consider Rivers of Love a linear system of behavior. This is not "cookbook lovemaking" "*Insert tab A, into slot B, then take item C and....*" That I have outlined it this way should be viewed only as a temporary convenience.

Ideally, our lovemaking is playful and ecstatic. This material is designed to be *fun.* If any of these exercises are not fun, *we should stop doing them.* We might find that they may become more appealing at another time, or in a different frame of mind. Or... perhaps not. In any event, we have enough duties, obligations, and deadlines in our lives. We can afford to leave these out of our lovemaking.

One of the best ways we can experience the essence of this work is to allow ourselves to laugh! If we choose to climax, we may notice that there is a point at which the physical release lends itself to

Anyone can be passionate,
but it takes real lovers to be silly.

Rose Franklin

laughter. We all look silly when we climax. This is good. During climax we can let our physical joy erupt into laughter. This bliss is our birthright.

In Daoist terms, we can transform our inner smile into outer belly laughter. If we choose not to climax, we can still release laughter during a "valley orgasm" or whenever our body requests it. We just should be sure to let our partner know that we're not laughing *at* her... that we are just happy. She'll get the idea.

Please remember that *learning* a skill takes time and can be frustrating. Skiing and surfing are also exhilarating and ecstatic, but not the first few times we try them. We can give ourselves plenty of room for the learning curve. (I know, practicing lovemaking can be hell, but try to suffer through it)

Also remember that while this is designed to be playful, sensitive emotional issues may arise and these can be very real. Although we may not understand what our partner is feeling, we should take the time to listen carefully, and if we can, validate her feelings. This can be an important part of our healing both as individuals, and as a couple.

As we gain experience (and because this is *ecstatic* and not *static*), we will find ourselves moving back and forth between convulsive explosions, numbed stupor, space travel, neon dreams, comatose sleep, emotional tenderness, oceans of electricity, and sweaty exhaustion. We will push the envelope. We will flow between Qi Release, Mirror Breathing, Ribbon Breath, Infinite Touch, profound intimacy, sexual fantasies, and drowning in bliss. Undoubtedly, on occasion, we will also encounter boredom, frustration, disconnect, and unplanned ejaculations.

Good. This is as exactly as it should be.

We can be patient with ourselves and kind to our partner.

Breath—Qigong

BREATH AND SEX

Have you ever noticed your lover or yourself holding your breath during lovemaking? Our breathing patterns are deeply involved with the quality of our sex life.

Many of us intuitively know that our breath is connected to our experience of sex and orgasm. Some people become aroused when the flow of oxygen to the brain is reduced. This is not a new idea. As a result of his own observations centuries ago, Leonardo da Vinci concluded that the breath was responsible for our ability to have erections.

Many people assume that when someone is holding their breath during sex that they are stifling the flow of energy in their body. While this may be true to a degree, this explanation does not seem entirely accurate. It is doubtful that so many people instinctively attempt to *reduce* pleasurable sensations in their bodies during lovemaking. A more plausible explanation may be that when we hold our breath during lovemaking we are actually attempting to *increase* our arousal.

How can this be?

Our brain stem controls our primary biological functions of respiration, immunity, and reproduction. By increasing the relative amount of carbon dioxide in our brain stem it seems that we may be modulating our levels of sexual arousal. We may actually be holding our breath as a way to self-medicate, as a kind of respiratory aphrodisiac.

While this pattern is common and may temporarily increase our arousal, ultimately it can reinforce our habituated patterns of goal oriented lovemaking and erotic immersion. Qigong offers us a different and even more powerful way of using our breath to create states of deep interactive bliss.

INTRODUCTION TO BREATH - QIGONG

As the Chinese word Qi (pronounced "chee") means *air* or *energy*. The word "Qigong" means *working with air*, or *working with energy*. Qigong is the Chinese art of *working with breath, energy and movement*. There are thousands of Qigong exercises, each one based on the building, movement, or draining of Qi.

Qigong originated in ancient China and became a favorite pastime of the Daoist and Buddhist monks. Legend has it that the man who brought Buddhism to China also brought exercises that later became the precursors to Qigong.

Qigong practices are sometimes divided into two categories. There are "Neidan" (inner elixir) practices and "Waidan" (outer elixir) practices. Neidan practices use the breath and are involved with subtle energetic movement. Waidan practices use muscular tension more than breath and are involved with strong physical exertion. The Qigong we are exploring in this book, both alone and with our partner, is Neidan Qigong.

A good foundation Neidan Qigong exercise is Small Heavenly Circuit (see page 132). This core practice can help us pack Qi Energy and retain Jing Essence as well as circulating energy in the body. Packing Qi Energy and retaining Jing Essence can aid in peace of mind and boost health and vitality. Once we are comfortable with the single cultivation practice we can begin doing dual cultivation with our partner.

If our partner and we are both doing Qigong together and coordinating our practice, then this is called "dual cultivation". And even if we are making love with our partner but we are the only person doing Qigong, then this is "single cultivation".

Probably the last thing we want to think about while making love is how we are breathing. That is why at first it is useful to practice our Qigong patterns by ourselves until we have ingrained those habits of breath and movement into our body. Once they have been trained into muscle memory, we can then slowly begin to incorporate them into our lovemaking.

So the more we practice these patterns while alone, the more intuitive these they will become. Once we have habituated ourselves to these patterns we can begin to use them when we are with our partner, either while practicing Qigong together or while making love.

If we are making love, we can do single cultivation practices on our own, even if our partner is involved in the cultivation. Indeed we could do our Qigong cultivation while making love and she might never know. She would always know if we were doing bodywork on her, but patterns of breath in our body can be much more subtle. See *Learning to Learn: Patience and Levels of Competence* (see page 107). Or if our partner is interested in dual cultivation we can begin to synchronize our Qigong and practice some of the exercises in this book.

We can also practice synchronized Qigong with our partner, while sitting or lying together. This can be very helpful as we learn how to cultivate.

Great lovemaking can exist on its own, without *any* Qigong or Qi Release. But we can improve even great lovemaking by adding Qigong and Qi Release to our intimate practices. Either one can have a powerful and profound effect on our physical health, not to mention the increased emotional connection with our partner.

Why Do Qigong?

The core philosophy of old China was, and is, called Daoism. Both Qigong and traditional Chinese medicine are the products of Daoist (and to a lesser extent, Buddhist) philosophy.

One of the goals of Daoist practice was the generation of physical health and longevity. The old Daoists were intensely curious and many of them were highly literate. They would experiment on themselves using the tools of breath, movement, herbs, food, and sexuality. They would then put their conclusions in writing and teach it to their students.

Qigong is not a religion; it is a practice and a philosophy of health. We do not need to be a Daoist in order to do Qigong any more than we must become a Hindu before doing yoga.

Qigong promotes health in numerous ways. These small daily practices in Qigong add up, day after day, year after year, and help us create a foundation of health in our lives.

For example, one important system of our body is our lymphatic system. Our lymphatic system allows us to remove toxins from our cells and gives our immune system the ability to kill pathogens.

Unlike the cardiovascular system, whose pump is the heart and arteries, our lymphatic system has no pump. The lymph pumps in our bodies are our breath and the movement of our muscles, the main components of Qigong practice.

Qigong has within it a kind of genius, the conclusions of thousands of years of observation and experimentation. Many of the tenets of Qigong have become supported by recent discoveries in science and Western medicine.

For instance, in Qigong, the process of cleansing our mouth with our tongue is thought to increase health and lifespan. At first glance this seems ludicrous. But recent scientific research has correlated gum disease in the mouth with increased risk of heart attack and stroke. Bacteria growing in the mouth cause gum disease and those bacteria can only thrive within a certain acid-alkaline ratio.

The Qigong practice of cleansing the mouth with the tongue and generating saliva neutralizes the ph of the mouth and prevents the accumulation of bacteria, thereby preventing cardiovascular disease. This would have especially been true in ancient China before the days of toothbrushes.

Another traditional Daoist practice is keeping the tongue firmly on the roof of the mouth while doing Qigong. In the process of keeping our tongue on the roof of our mouth the soft palate at the rear of the roof of the mouth is tightened and kept toned. A flaccid soft palate is what causes sleep apnea and snoring. Sleep apnea has also been correlated to heart attack, stroke, and early death.

There are many other examples of Qigong practices that make sense in the light of recent scientific research, including sexual practices.

WHY DO SEXUAL QIGONG WITH A PARTNER?

Not that we need science to justify pleasure, but there are plenty of scientific rationales for engaging in these practices with our lover.

For men, active sexuality tends to increase testosterone levels but ejaculation tends to decrease them. In terms of health, high levels of testosterone in men are correlated with lower rates of heart disease. This may be why classic Daoist texts recommend that men have active sex lives but limit their number of ejaculations.

In women, powerful sexuality and orgasms release the hormone oxytocin. Oxytocin is known to increase pleasure and is associated with bonding increased trust, and generosity in women. (Vasopressin seems to serve this function in men) Oxytocin is one of the few hormones that has a "positive feedback" mechanism in the body. What this means is that oxytocin tends to create more oxytocin.

Oxytocin is not only released during sexual activity, but also during hugging, nursing, eye gazing, and even when women simply hear their lover's voice on the telephone. This may be why the touch of Qi Release (see page 143) and the eye gazing of Infinity practices (see page 241) are particularly powerful for women.

There are many other hormones released during pair bonding, but these are just a few examples of many as to why these practices are so good for us.

And finally, doing Qigong while making love turbo charges the Qigong practice while simultaneously enhancing the pleasure of the lovemaking. Really, the best reason to do sexual Qigong with a partner is because it feels wonderful. The ultimate purpose of our sexuality is to exalt us, and sexual Qigong can help in that endeavor.

QIGONG ALONE
Small Heavenly Circuit / River Cart

Small Heavenly Circuit is a foundation piece of Qigong practice. It has other names such as River Cart, Microcosmic Orbit, and Small Universe.

Small Heavenly Circuit can be done anytime, while working, resting, driving, or making love. It can be done while standing, sitting, or laying down. No matter which position we are in, the spine is kept relaxed and long. The cervical (neck) and lumbar (low back) spinal curves are flattened. The spine is lengthened on the "in" breath and kept long on the "out" breath.

If standing, feet are shoulder width apart and parallel. Knees are bent. Shoulders are down and forward. The muscles are allowed to sink on the out-breath but the body stays erect and the spine stays long.

To begin, inhale through the nose with the tongue up visualizing energy running up the spine. Tighten and relax the perineum (the area between the scrotum and the anus), Exhale out the mouth, with the tongue down visualizing energy moving down the midline on the front of the body. Remember, the spine is lengthened on the in-breath and kept long on the out-breath. Women should not lift up on the pelvic floor (kegel exercises) during menstruation.

So the process looks something like this:

INHALE	TIGHTEN PERINEUM—RELAX	EXHALE

Through the nose ———————————————————Out the mouth
Tongue up———————————————————————Tongue down
Up the spine—————————————————————Down the front

Please note that there are many different variations to Small Heavenly Circuit. In some variations the perineum remains tightened the whole time, and in others different areas of the perineum and anus are tightened in a specific sequence.

In some systems the breath is held while completing the circuit, in others, not. In some systems the energy goes up the front and down the back. If we research we will undoubtedly learn other many ways of doing Small Heavenly Circuit and that is fine.

One of the best ways to incorporate Small Heavenly Circuit into our daily life is to create a psychological trigger, to "anchor" or remind us to the practice. We can use almost anything as a trigger to anchor us to the practice. Some people will do Small Heavenly Circuit anytime they are in their car resting at a stop sign or a traffic light. Others will do it whenever they touch a doorknob. An effective way to incorporate Small Heavenly Circuit is to buy a digital watch that we can program to beep every hour. Whenever we hear that watch beep we lengthen our spine, relax our shoulders and jaw, and active the circuit. After doing this for a few weeks we will find ourselves doing Small Heavenly Circuit a few seconds *before* the watch beeps, our unconscious mind having correctly gauged the time between reminders. If we keep the watch next to the bed we may even notice ourselves doing Small Heavenly Circuit in our sleep! At this stage we have fully woven Qigong practice into the fiber of our being. This is the most powerful way to incorporate Qigong into our lives. As we develop more skills we may find ourselves automatically doing Small Heavenly Circuit as we become aroused. With this we can learn to spread the erotic energy that is our life force and use it to perfuse the tissue throughout our whole body. This marvelous energy need not remain trapped in our genitals.

REVERSE FLOW

Reverse Flow is an alternative way to move erotic energy through our bodies while making love.

In Qigong, our normal mode of moving energy is to bring energy into our bodies on the *inhale*, and to move energy out of our bodies on the *exhale*. In Reverse Flow we do the opposite. We move energy *out* of our body on the inhale and bring it *into* our body on the exhale. The feeling of Reverse Flow is softer and more expanding and permeating than the more directed energy flow that we may experience in Small Heavenly Circuit.

Reverse Flow can be used as a softer and subtler way of experiencing the erotic flow of energy in our body. We use it to help us relax around any place in our body that feels inordinately tight or has been difficult to soften energetically.

QI GONG WITH A PARTNER
Breathing and Rapport

Rapport is a verbal and subtle form of non-verbal communication that arises when we are "in synch" with someone else. When we have strong rapport with our partner, our breath will naturally synchronize with hers. This can be a powerful tool and is commonly used in many Daoist and Tantric exercises. Because rapport is an important component of sexual activity, Mirror Breathing is a good way to begin to deepen our rapport with our partner.

Mirror Breathing

Mirror breathing is what we do naturally when we have physical rapport with our partner. With friends and lovers we will often do this unconsciously, literally mirroring each other's breath and sometimes even mirroring each other's posture, verbal cadence, and body language. When we Mirror Breathe we inhale as our partner is inhaling and exhale as our partner is exhaling. Mirror Breath is used to create bonding and intimacy. In Rivers of Love, the opposite of Mirror Breathing is called Flow Breathing. We use Flow Breathing when we want to send and receive energy.

Fig. 1. Mirror Breathing

Flow Breathing

Flow Breathing is a more challenging but equally useful type of breathing. Flow Breathing uses an alternating breath, in other words we are inhaling when our partner is exhaling, and vice versa. Because we naturally mirror our partner's breath when in deep arousal, Flow breathing has to be done somewhat consciously and is more of an advanced technique than Mirror Breath. Flow Breath is used to send and receive energy, often to transmit feelings, sensations, or emotions to our partner. The sending and receiving of energy in Qigong is called emitting and absorbing Qi. It is especially useful while doing Meridian Energetics (Five Element) advanced techniques.

Fig. 2. Flow Breathing   **Fig. 3. Flow Breathing**

Emitting and Absorbing Qi

There is a saying in traditional Chinese medicine: *The Qi follows the thinking.* When we want to *emit* energy in Qigong, we *exhale* as we visualize the energy moving out of our body. Sometimes when we do this we are "tonifying" our partner. When we want to *absorb* Qi, we do so on while *inhaling*, visualizing it moving into us. Either partner can "tonify" the other. If we are making love with our partner and we wish to circulate the Qi, we *imagine* the energy flowing smoothly through our body, or that of our partner. If we come across an area in ourselves that feels tight or is not conducive to the feeling of Qi flowing, we gently imagine the Qi flowing *around* that area, gradually melting it like ice. Sometimes colors will emerge from our visualizations.

This tonification can also be done via the genitals while making love. Either partner can send energy to the other through their genitals.

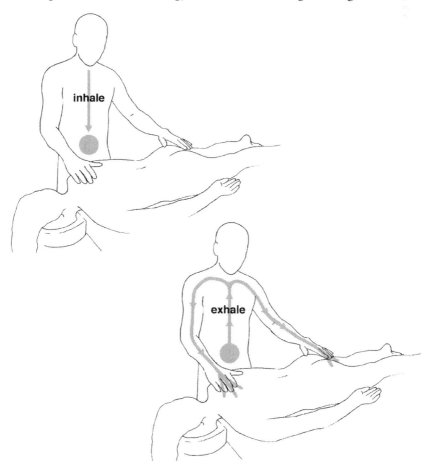

Fig. 4 & 5. Emitting Qi: The man "tonifying" the woman

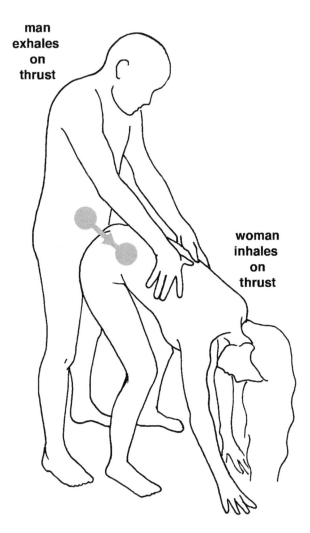

**man
exhales
on
thrust**

**woman
inhales
on
thrust**

Fig. 6. Emitting Qi: The man "tonifying" the woman in communion

Visualization and Color

There are powerful and sophisticated techniques for visualization that couples, but unfortunately they are outside of the scope of this book. I will describe them in *Rivers of Love: Sexuality in the Heart of Healing,* which will be available soon.

QIGONG PARTNER TECHNIQUES

We are offering here a few examples of Qigong partner techniques but there are many others. All single person Qigong breathing techniques can be adapted for use by couples. Both Neidan (inner elixir) and Waidan (outer elixir) techniques work very well in a Rivers of Love setting if each partner is comfortable with doing them alone first. Here are a few useful patterns:

Small Heavenly Circuit for Two

Small Heavenly Circuit can be done while making love from any position. This practice will energize and potentize our lovemaking. We can coordinate the practice with our partner or do it on our own.

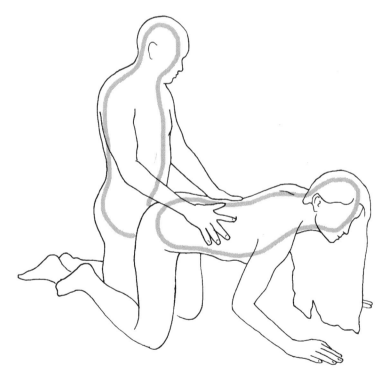

Fig. 7. Small Heavenly Circuit (for Two)

Fig. 8. Larger Heavenly Circuit

Fig. 9. Waterfall Breathing

Larger Heavenly Circuit (for Two)

Larger Heavenly Circuit is Small Heavenly Circuit coordinated as a couple, creating one large circuit between two people. It can go in either direction (up or down either partner's spine) and can be done from any position: Dragon, Tiger, Phoenix, Lotus, or Yin Yang. Another coordinated Qigong practice is called Waterfall Breathing.

Waterfall Breathing

Waterfall Breathing is two people doing Small Heavenly Circuit together but mirroring each other's energy flow. The flow goes up each person's spine then falls over the top of the head and down the front like a waterfall. Waterfall Breathing can be done with a Mirror or a Flow breath. When we have practiced and become very comfortable with Larger Heavenly Circuit and Waterfall Breathing and wish to enhance our intimacy we might try Ribbon Breathing.

Ribbon Breathing

Ribbon Breathing is an energetic weaving technique that weaves energy back and forth between partners. Ribbon Breathing uses a

Flow breath between partners, so as the man is exhaling the woman is inhaling and vice versa.

Ribbon Breathing can take a bit of practice for two people to gain competence in it. Please note that the gender roles can easily be reversed in this practice. It is as follows:

1) The man the man withdraws his penis he inhales from the earth through the floor of his pelvis (*acupoint huiyin / ren 1*) or through the bottom of his feet (*acupoint yongquan / kidney 1*), filling the floor of his pelvis with Earth Qi.

2) As he thrusts in he then exhales this Qi visualizing energy moving out his genitals and into hers. As he does this, the woman is inhaling and visualizing his energy moving into her yoni.

3) As he withdraws she then exhales the Qi out her lower abdomen (*acupoint qihai / ren 6*) as he inhales it into his lower abdomen (*acupoint qihai / ren 6*).

4) Thrusting, he then exhales out his chest (*acupoint shanzhong / ren 12*) and she inhales into hers.

5) Withdrawing, she exhales out her throat (*acupoint lianquan / ren 23*) and he inhales into his.

6) Thrusting into her, he exhales out between his eyebrows (*acupoint yin tang*) and she inhales into hers, filling her head with Qi.

7) As he withdraws she exhales out the top of her head (*acupoint baihui / du 20*) and he inhales into his, filling his head with Qi.

8) As they both relaxing, he exhales the energy out his body and returning it back into the earth.

They can then repeat the pattern, reverse the flow of energy by having the woman "give" to the man as she thrusts, do something different, or if they are comfortable enough they can slip into Paliuli (see page 183).

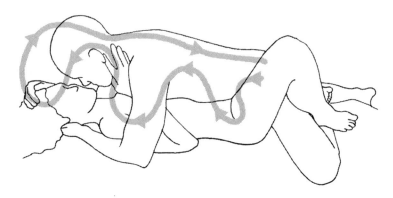

Fig. 10. Ribbon Breathing

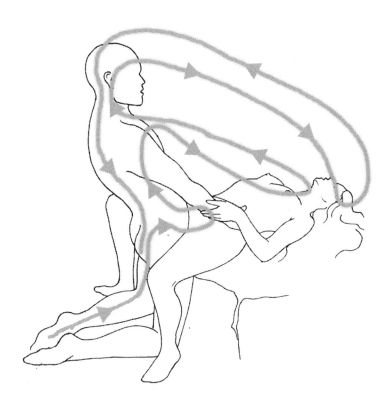

Fig. 11. Modified Ribbon Breathing

Touch—Qi Release

INTRODUCTION TO TOUCH—QI RELEASE BODYWORK

The arena of touch can be very charged for us as human beings. Many of our interactions with others are defined by touch, or lack of it.

There are different touch boundaries for the different categories of people in our lives. The only relationships where there are little or no touch boundaries are the relationship between a parent and an infant and the relationship between lovers.

This book is not about the social and interpersonal repercussions of touch. But it *is* a platform from which we can take a normal sexual experience and, using an expanded touch and breath; turn that sexual experience into something deeper and more profound.

We refer to Rivers of Love bodywork as Qi Release because that is what happens during a Rivers of Love session: Qi, or energy, is released. All Rivers of Love bodywork is considered Qi Release with the exception of Infinity practices (see Wei Wu Wei). We will elaborate more on Qi Release later.

There is but one temple in the Universe…
and that is the human body. Nothing is
holier than that high form. We touch heaven
when we lay our hand on the human body.

THOMAS CARLYLE

To lovers, touch is a metamorphosis.
All the parts of their bodies seem to change, and
seem to become something different and better.

JOHN CHEEVER

Rivers of Love bodywork is done without draping and with a considerable amount of oil covering an appropriately smooth surface. The slippery nature of the oil is what creates the desired sensations in our partner. Because our arms are often between our partner's body and the surface on which she is laying, the work is usually done on an undraped massage table or on vinyl that is spread out over a bed. Thus, the surface that our partner is laying on should be smooth (like vinyl) as opposed to textured (like fabric or carpet). While Rivers of Love bodywork can be done on a normal bed or futon draped with sheets and a blanket, it is not nearly as pleasurable or effective.

Rivers of Love is the melding of a healing touch with an erotic touch shared between lovers.

Safety

If we are not physically capable of giving or receiving regular massage or bodywork then we should not be giving or receiving Rivers of Love bodywork.

In worship, we anoint our partner thoroughly. We anoint her head to toe with oil, including her feet. We can use a lot of oil. The same oil that makes it so pleasurable also makes it dangerous. Oil is slippery. Oily skin on vinyl is even slipperier. Oily bottoms can even make toilet seats quite slippery. Oily feet are dangerous, especially on smooth surfaces. *We must wipe oil off of feet before entering a smooth-floored surface such as a wood or tiled floor.*

Gravity works… Be Very Careful.

We worship our Goddess in order to improve our quality of life and enhance our health and well-being. Injuries can reduce quality of life, health, and well-being significantly.

I repeat: *Gravity works… Be Very Careful.*

The Importance of Posture

If we want to "Worship the Goddess" without putting our Chiropractor into a higher tax bracket, then we will definitely need to watch our posture while doing Qi Release. Qi Release can be physically demanding for the person giving and it is very important that we take care not to injure ourselves. Low back pain will not enhance a romantic evening.

If we are unaccustomed to doing bodywork, study the bodywork sections of this book very slowly and pace yourself. If we are uncertain about our *ability* to do bodywork, we *must* have a physical evaluation by a licensed health care professional before proceeding. It may also help us to take a class on massage to acquaint ourselves with proper body alignment.

The most important part of posture for us as body-workers is how our weight is distributed. Our knees should be bent and our hips should be as low as we can comfortably manage. Allowing swivel in our hips will allow our upper torso to move in a fluid way. Keeping our knees bent will keep the weight on top of our legs and keep undue strain away from our lower back. If our hips are extremely low then we will only effectively be able to contact our beloved with our arms. But often when we wish to include parts of our torso as points of contact, we will be more bent over with our weight resting on our partner.

It is *very* easy for us to hurt ourselves if we are doing bodywork improperly. If we take good care of ourselves, our partner will thank us for it. Proper posture can help assure our physical safety, but in order to create a positive experience for our partner and us we also must consider the aspect of emotional safety,

Body Armor

Our emotions and memories are rooted in our musculature and in our viscera. The language of our emotions is written in our patterns of muscle tension and neurotransmitter release. It is impossible to feel any strong emotion without simultaneously experiencing a specific pattern of muscle tension in our body. When we do deep

And the day came when the risk to remain tight in a bud was more painful than the risk it took to blossom.

ANAIS NIN

tissue bodywork such as Bone Washing, we can release muscles from their "set point" of tension. This change of set point releases Qi that is trapped in the muscle channel. Muscles that are released can also trigger memories. When we release Qi from the muscle channels we can release the emotion and the muscle memory that is stored in that Qi. Rivers of Love can release stored memories and awaken repressed memories. Because of this release of energy and possible awakening of emotions and memories; it can be liberating, traumatic, or anything in between. Either partner, the giver or the receiver may be affected although it is much more common for the receiver to experience strong emotional release or triggered memories. Any deep tissue bodywork can resurrect repressed memories, but adding the sensations of deep arousal can "turbo charge" the experience. Navigating the results can require tact, skill and differentiation.

In the same way our posture can hold emotional patterns within us; those patterns, however unpleasant or dysfunctional, can also be considered a kind of emotional "safety net". When we rearrange the muscular and energetic patterns in our partner's body through deep arousal combined with deep bodywork, her "safety net" may be "rearranged" or may even feel as if it has been removed. She may feel vulnerable. Not being used to this new and more relaxed pattern; she may feel out of her comfort zone. This can be compared to the feeling we get when wearing someone else shoes where the patterns of wear are different than our own. Indeed she may not know where to "put her feet". She may find herself in the unfamiliar position of inhabiting "someone else's" body.

This need not always be unpleasant. Indeed, our partner will often appreciate her renewed sense of energy and deep gratification in her body when her pattern of muscular tension has been changed.

But this situation also contains the potential for upheaval, disorientation, and emotional confusion. See *Boundaries and Sexual Abuse Issues* on page 87.

These emotional and physiological changes can create opportunities for intimacy, dialogue, and even emotionally oriented work.

Emotionally Oriented Work with our Partner

Couples can also use numerous emotionally based techniques during a Rivers of Love session such as Holotropic Breathwork, Hellerwork or Hakomi Therapy. While it is not our job to be a therapist for our partner, highly aroused states hold powerful opportunities for our healing. For most people the only person who will be present when they are in a highly aroused state will be their partner. This partner could turn out to be the best, or worst, person to do this with.

If we choose to do therapeutic style exercises with our partner, excessively sticky or complex issues that arise should be referred to a professional. And anyone with significant or suspected trauma in their past should seek out professional help.

Foreplay: Circling In for a Loving Landing

Much of the material in this book is concerned with giving and receiving, i.e. one partner is more active and the other is more receptive. ("Passive" is not an accurate term for what happens when one is receiving sexual pleasure) Because this book is for men and is concerned with "Worshipping the Goddess", much of the material is geared towards the men "giving" and the women "receiving".

Practically speaking this often will not be the case. With that in mind, the book *Rivers of Love: Sexuality in the Heart of Healing* will explain in detail ways that couples can mutually enhance physical and emotional healing, and will address ways that the woman can please the man.

If we are to truly worship our Goddess we have to totally rethink everything we know about foreplay. Is foreplay something that we've been enduring just so that we can get to the *real* sex? If so then we have missed the point. If we want to worship our partner in the manner of a God, befitting a Goddess, we need to do more than just warm her up. Foreplay is not about getting our partner *aroused,*

Mrs. Robinson, do you think we could say a few words to each other first this time?

DUSTIN HOFFMAN IN *THE GRADUATE*

Anything worth doing well is worth doing slowly.

GYPSY ROSE LEE

it is about *opening her heart*. We don't open her heart by talking (although we can); we open her heart with our touch. But when we touch her, it is different than our "normal" touch. This touch is permeated with our presence; *we are present when it happens*. Our hands become an extension of our heart, of the depth of our love. We take our time. We let touch linger.

Of course, we're men. When we begin to be sexual there is a part of us that wants to just *hurry up and get it on*! But if we wait, if we are patient, and if our antennae are attuned to Her: We may discover landscapes, terrain, and intimacy that we never knew existed. In order to get beyond what we think sex is *really* about, i.e. orgasm, we have to *want* something more. We must open ourselves to possibilities. We can choose our responses, rather than have our scripting choose them for us.

When we take our time making love it deepens her level of trust. And once she trusts she can begin to open. We want to slowly and sweetly encourage her to open all of herself. She *wants* us to help her open. We can help her open every muscle, every cell, to flood it with sweet erotic energy. When she is open, *really* open, then her heart opens. When her heart is open, *then* she is aroused, and *then* she can receive us. She wants to receive us, but first she must feel connected. We men come to intimacy through arousal, but our partner comes to arousal through intimacy. In order for our partner's sweet yoni to blossom fully so that we can taste her nectar, her heart also needs a safe place from which it can blossom. We can hold space and prepare the ground for that blossoming.

Men are different than women energetically in that we don't necessarily need our hearts open in order to feel aroused. But our partner is very much an energetic creature and she craves certain kinds of energetic stimulation. The Chinese have taught for thousands of years about energetic channels in the body called "meridians". When we are opening our partner's heart with our touch we do it by stimulating these meridians. Women need their meridians stimulated while making love if we want their energy to flow. The simplest way to do this is just to *keep our hands moving*. The meridians cover the whole

Some men know that a light touch of the tongue,
running from a woman's toes to her ears, lingering
in the softest way possible in various places in
between, given often enough and sincerely enough
would add immeasurably to world peace.

MARIANNE WILLIAMSON

body, and when our hands *slowly* glide across her skin these meridians are activated. When her heart has opened and she is aroused her deepest primal energy begins to flow. The Chinese call this energy "Qi" and Qi can be channeled in all sorts of ways. For Qi to flow in powerful ways our empathic antennae need to be fine-tuned; we need to *pay attention.*

We can also use our hands as erogenous zones… in other words we can enjoy ourselves while we are touching our partner. We can experience pleasure through our hands. (See Touching to Receive on page 154)

While doing bodywork, the best way to open our partner's heart and prepare her for communion is to *circle in for a loving landing.* What this means is that we slowly work our touch toward her center. We work from the outside in. The places we *want* to touch first are the ones we touch *last.* We begin at fingers and toes and slowly move toward her center. We take our time. No, we *really* take our time. Our touch should begin as smoothly and softly as possible. We are facilitating her flowering but we are not actually doing very much at all. We are simply holding space so that her inner passion is allowed to emerge. We are not *creating* that passion; we are *facilitating* it. The space we create and hold, our skill and intention, and our delayed gratification all encourages her to fully embody and awaken her wild and primal Goddess. We sense what she's feeling. We feel what she's feeling. We feel her heart open and her passion build. We connect our heart with hers and drive her insane with passion.

Soft and Intense

We can also use our hands and mouth in seemingly conflicting ways to generate arousal in our partner. A pleasant way to do this is to bite her neck carefully but firmly, as our hands *very* gently stroke her yoni. The teeth should be firm (think of lions mating) just short of pain, and the hands should be as soft and gentle as moist silk.

Yang and Yin Hands

In Rivers of Love bodywork (Qi Release) there are times when one of our hands is more active and the other is more passive. The active hand is typically called the "yang" and the supportive or softer hand is called the "yin" hand. We will refer to them this way from now on.

Touching to Give

When we "Worship the Goddess" we are involved in *touching to give*. In touching to give we allow ourselves to be a vehicle, a conduit for the movement of our partner's energy. The *intention* of our touch is someone else's exaltation, to increase their health, well being, and, from a Daoist perspective, to ultimately discover their destiny.

Touching to Receive

Sometimes, less frequently, when we "Worship the Goddess" we are *touching to receive*. When we touch to receive we touch for *our* pleasure, for the pleasure that we receive from our hands, arms, chest, cheeks or lips. We can learn to *receive* pleasure from touch. It only takes a minor shift in perspective to activate this unique way of receiving pleasure. In the same way we can enjoy the sensation of letting our lips linger on our partner's flower, we can also enjoy the pleasure of feeling our hands glide across her body. We are capable of receiving pleasure from more than just our genitals. Our whole body is also capable of receiving pleasure.

RIVERS OF LOVE QI RELEASE (BODYWORK) STYLES

Rivers of Love Qi Release

Rivers of Love Qi Release is the art of massaging our partner during highly aroused states. We do this as a form of worship and energy exchange, to enhance our partner's health and well being, to arouse her and us, and to create ever deeper states of bonding and emotional connection.

There are two basic categories of Qi Release: Broad Brush Qi

Release and Narrow Brush Qi Release.

Broad Brush Qi Release: Temple Bodywork

Broad Brush Qi Release, also called Temple Bodywork, is a form of worship, a gift given from us to our partner. Temple Bodywork can be done quickly or slowly, although slow is usually better. We can experiment, increasing the speed if we choose. In Temple Bodywork we maintain maximum body contact between giver and receiver, creating a nurturing and attentive feeling for our partner. We do not merely worship the skin of our partner with our hands; we wrap and embrace as much of her essence with as much of our own body as possible. We *become* reverence. Our reverence initiates the gradual, controlled, and consecrated arousal of our beloved. Not only do we arouse our partner and open her heart, but we also generate and move Qi in her body. This Qi is generated, held in place, and moved through our mutual focus and intention. Our forearms and shoulders are used extensively, as well as our torso and even our legs. We initiate and direct her erotic energy *while holding our own*. We maintain contact not only over the upper surface of our partner's body but also move our hands and arms between her body and the table or bed. Temple Bodywork can arouse our partner and facilitate the opening of her heart.

Women and men can show up differently when they make love, they often speak different languages. Women often need their heart opened in order to awaken their erotic body. Men often need a lot of physical contact in order to awaken their erotic body. Temple Bodywork can create a common language that both parties understand, a fusion of male and female styles of erotic manifestation.

Temple Bodywork creates an opportunity for both partners to get what they want and need from their lovemaking. The lingering attention that we bring to our partner nurtures her and opens her heart as well as her yoni. She feels held both physically and emotionally. The intense sexuality and large surface area of contact feeds our need as men to experience powerful physical contact with our partner.

Narrow Brush Qi Release: Bone Washing

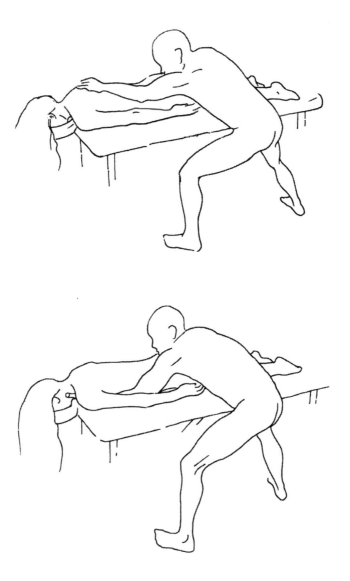

Fig. 12 & 13. Broadbrush Qi Release
Note arm under torso in bottom illustration.

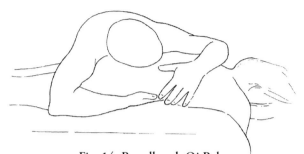

Fig. 14. Broadbrush Qi Release
The right hand is between the body and the table.

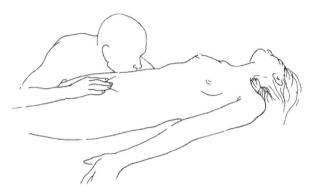

Fig. 15. Broadbrush Qi Release
Note that the left arm is between the body and the table.

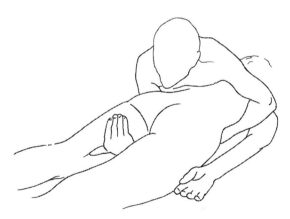

Fig. 16. Broadbrush Qi Release
Note that both arms are between the body and the table.

Fig. 17. Broadbrush Qi Release

Narrow Brush Qi Release is also called Bone Washing. While Bone Washing is different from the Broad Brush Temple Bodywork, they can easily flow into each other; they exist on a continuum. A Rivers of Love session will include a lot of both.

Bone Washing impacts the fascia and connective tissue of the body. If we look at a sirloin steak and we see the silver tissue between sections of meat, we are looking at connective tissue. Like that sirloin, we too have connective tissue surrounding the muscle in our bodies. Recent research has suggested that the connective tissue between our muscles works as an electrical feedback system, much like a computer semi-conductor. Some even claim that this is the mechanism through which acupuncture meridians are activated.

Bone Washing can be unpleasant if not done correctly. In Bone Washing there is "good" pain and "bad" pain. We can differentiate good pain from the bad pain because the good pain *"hurts so good"* and the bad pain just hurts. The more aroused our partner is, the more pressure she will be comfortable with. *When in doubt, we should err on the side of caution and not work too deep. If our partner is tightening her body from the intensity of the pressure then the Qi has stopped moving and the process becomes counter-productive.* We want to stay in the "good" pain and avoid the "bad" pain. We keep her in "good" pain by controlling how much pressure we use and how quickly we move.

Bone Washing is slow and intentional. The slower it is done, the better the results. We only move as quickly as our partner's body "tells" us to. We wait for the muscle being released to show us how fast to move. Other parts of us, such as our tongue, fingers on the other hand, etcetera, may be moving quickly, but the part of our body doing the bone washing moves very slowly.

It may require a certain amount of hand strength to bone wash properly, particularly thumb and finger strength; hence it may be a bit easier for men to be the giver than for women.

When we Bone Wash we are rearranging our partner's physical structure and energetic flow. The muscles of our body are surrounded with a "sheath" of connective tissue. This "sheath" of connective tissue surrounding the muscles often runs longitudinally along the length of our limbs. Grooves are created lengthwise where the muscles lay along side each other. In traditional Chinese medicine these areas are called the *muscle channels*. In Bone Washing we run our hands along these longitudinal grooves; locating the muscle channels. The energy of the body has a tendency to become trapped in the grooves and fascia of these muscle channels. Once we have found these grooves we push along the channel, typically pressed against bone (hence the name). We never press perpendicular to the skin toward the bone. Instead we "plow" laterally along the connective tissue and "dredge" up this trapped Qi.

In Rivers of Love, Bone Washing is only done while our partner is in a highly aroused state. Her arousal and heart opening are facilitated with Temple bodywork. Before her heart is opened and she is highly aroused we do Temple bodywork. Only when we are very sure that the Qi is moving strongly throughout her body before we begin to Bone Wash.

During Bone Washing a highly aroused partner can release tremendous amounts of energy. Because our emotions are strongly linked to our patterns of muscle tension, emotional as well as energetic release can occur. See *Body Armor* on page 146.

When Qi Release is done properly, our partner can feel wonderful, sexy, and energetically alive. Temple Bodywork produces remarkable results when combined with affection, gratitude, and awareness.

RIVERS OF LOVE QI RELEASE (BODYWORK) TECHNIQUES

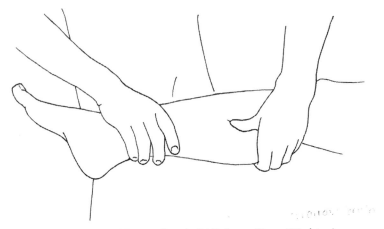

Fig. 18. Narrow Brush Qi Release (Bone Washing)
The left hand (the "yang" hand) in this drawing is Bone Washing.
The right hand is the "yin" passive hand.

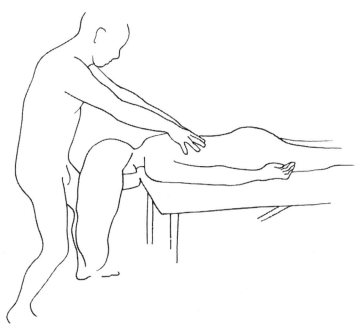

Fig. 19. Narrow Brush Qi Release (Bone Washing)
The thumbs are Bone Washing along the sides of the spine.

The Straight Release

The Straight Release is a Narrow Brush technique that can be done anywhere on our partner's body except the eyes, the front part of the throat, the breasts, the abdomen, the genitals, or the backs of the knees. The Straight Release is done with the fingers, thumb, and (in advanced techniques), with the knuckles or elbow.

The Straight Release follows the contours of our lover's body, staying in the grooves where muscle meets muscle or between muscle and bone. (See *Narrow Brush Qi Release: Bone Washing* on page 158)

The Neck Sweep

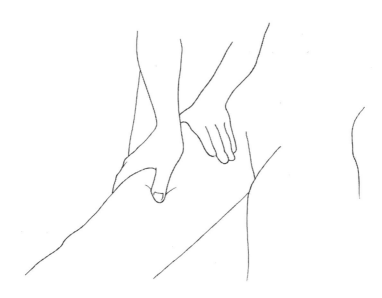

Fig. 20. The Straight Release (Bone Washing)
The right hand in this drawing is the "yang" active hand.
The left hand is the "yin" passive hand.

The Neck Sweep is a combination of Broad and Narrow Brush Qi Release. The Neck Sweep opens, extends, and lengthens the neck, creating an exquisite erotic vulnerability for our partner. The more surface contact we have with our partner during the Neck Sweep the safer, cradled, and more aroused she will feel. We worship her through the exquisite stimulation of her cervical nerve endings and those on her scalp.

The Neck Sweep is done when our partner is laying face up and we are standing at her head.

We sweep the right side of our partner's neck with our right hand and the left side of her neck with our left hand.

When sweeping her neck the fingers of the Yang (sweeping) hand are pointed up toward the ceiling. The sweep begins with the flat of the palm against the back of the neck near the shoulder. The fingers remain upright and the hand sweeps toward the ear. At the beginning of the sweep the palm is flat against the neck, but as our hand moves toward her ear the palm moves more in the direction of facing you. When we finish, the pinkie side of our palm is all that remains in contact with her neck.

When sweeping we want to feel each vertebrae moving as independently as possible. The cervical curve is accentuated and the head will naturally roll away from the sweeping Yang hand.

If we want to increase the arousal for our partner, we can let the middle joints of our fingers on the Yang hand fold across the transverse processes (side) of her neck, so that while our palm is on the back part of her neck, our fingers caress and front side and transverse her carotid and jugular vessels on the front part of her neck, moving up toward her jaw. Once we have swept past her neck toward the back of her head we can reach up with our fingers and massage her scalp. (See *Opening Heaven* on page 216)

Done in a rhythmic way the neck sweep can help in releasing the Yang Qi that gathers in the upper body from stress or sexual arousal.

The Neck Cradle

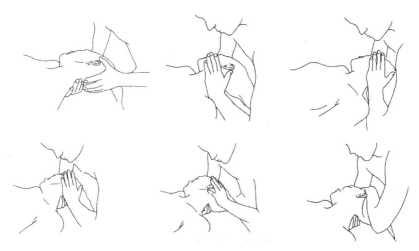

Fig. 21. The Neck Sweep (Broad Brush)
The right hand in this drawing is doing the Neck Cradle
immediately after the left hand sweeps the neck

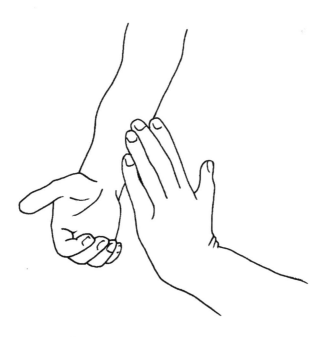

Fig. 22. The Neck Sweep (Broad Brush) Hand Movement

While sweeping her neck with our Yang hand we should also cradle and support our lover's head with our Yin (opposite) hand. The Yin hand (the right hand in the illustration) cradles the neck under the occiput (back of the head), allowing as much of the head and face to rest on our left forearm as possible. Just as we are finishing the neck sweep with our Yang hand, the fingers of our yin hand pull perpendicular to the tendons on either side of her neck, parallel to the back of her hairline. We are actually squeezing the back of her neck with our yin hand a split second after the Yang hand sweeps the neck.

Fig. 23. The Neck Cradle

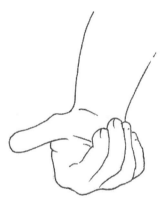

Fig. 24. The Neck Cradle Hand Movement

The Spider Sweep

The Spider Sweep is a Narrow Brush Qi Release technique that is different than other Narrow Brush techniques in that it is done rather quickly. The Spider Sweep extends our lovers neck and reinforces her natural curve there. When we do the Spider Sweep we articulate each vertebra in her neck encouraging them to move independently. We cradle the back of her head in our palms and roll our fingertips along the back of her neck rippling them symmetrically toward the top of her head. We repeat this rhythmically allowing her neck to ripple, arching and dipping, flowing like a wave. We can finish the rather rapid Spider Sweep with the slow release of Heaven's Cradle.

Fig. 25. The Spider Sweep

Fig. 26. The Spider Sweep Hand Movement

Fig. 27. The Spider Sweep Hand Movement

Heaven's Cradle

Heaven's Cradle is named after the acupuncture point *tianzhu / urinary bladder 10* ("heaven's pillow") located at the base of the skull. We Cradle Heaven after the Spider Sweep when our fingers reach the base of her skull. All four fingers are brought together supporting and hooking the occipital ridge on the centerline. We then pull the hands apart laterally (toward the outside), each hand moving toward the corresponding ear. As we do this we allow her head to sink toward the table. This Bone Washing releases Qi that may be trapped along the base of her skull and retrain the muscles in her neck to relax. This relaxation allows the Yang Qi to move up her spine and fill her head as her arousal increases.

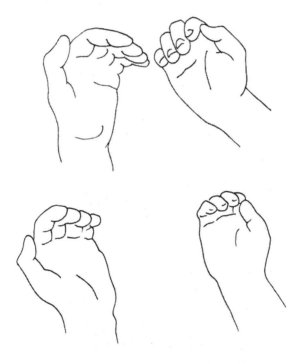

Figs. 28 & 29. Heavens Cradle - Hand Position
The hands move away from each other

Crane Exposes Her Neck

Our partner is laying face up. From our position standing at our partner's side, we lightly bite or suck her opposite nipple. Our arms can be above or below our lover's body, i.e. on top of her or between her body and the table. Either way, our hands meet at the high point of the shoulder muscle *jianjing / gall bladder 21* called "shoulder well". From jianjing we Bone Wash with our fingers, releasing the tension in her shoulder by moving our hands apart. One hand moves toward the head and the other hand moves toward the shoulder. The area between the spine and the shoulder blades on the side closest to us can be released also.

Fig. 30. Crane Exposes Neck–Arms Above

Fig. 31. Crane Exposes Neck–ArmsBelow The hands move away from each other

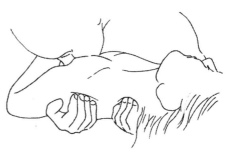

Fig. 32. Crane Exposes Neck–ArmsBelow

The Serpent Stretch

While doing the Serpent Stretch we make sure that our partner's back and the table below her are both well oiled.

The Serpent Stretch is done as our partner lays face up on the massage table. Each meridian and organ in the body corresponds to acupuncture points along either side of the spine. The Serpent Stretch elongates the spine while stimulating these points. When we do the Serpent Stretch we strive to have each of our partner's vertebrae articulating independently, nourishing her spine and the surrounding meridians and muscles with Qi and blood.

In the Serpent Stretch our arms are between our partner's back and the table. Our fingers are hooked facing up as we slowly and deliberately release the tension from our partner's spine. We Bone Wash lengthwise along the grooves on either side of her backbone.

The Serpent Stretch from Above

The Serpent Stretch from above is done as we stand at the head of the massage table. The Serpent Stretch from Above lengthens our partner's spine in the direction of her head. We are literally up to our shoulders in our Goddess. As we Bone Wash up her spine we lean back and pull our arms move up her spine toward her head. We let her spine ripple like a snake's, deliciously releasing the Qi that is stuck between her vertebrae and in the surrounding muscle tissue.

After we have made a few passes up her spine we can do the same move but as our hands get closer to her shoulders we can separate them, and rather than releasing right alongside the spine, we bring our hands out toward her shoulder blades, releasing the tender areas just inside them.

We can also use just one hand to elongate her spine, the other can support her head in the Neck Cradle. Our body positioning while doing this can determine the level of intimacy and arousal generated. The more surface contact between our partner and us, the more intimate this will feel. We can have her head nuzzled against our chest as we lean over her. And if we suck and lick her nipples as we do the Serpent Stretch we may increase her arousal.

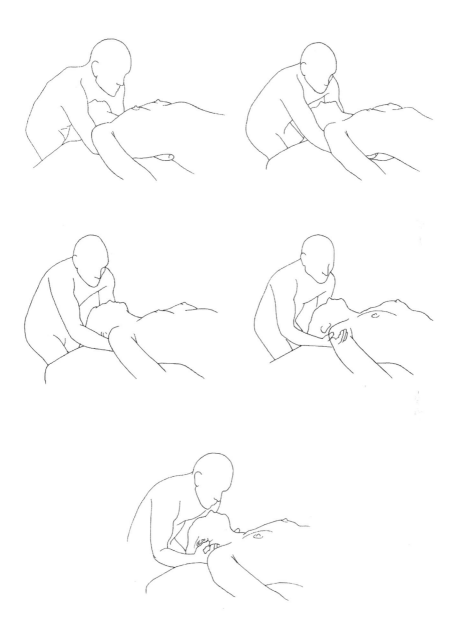

Figs. 33-37. Serpent Stretch from Above
Note the position of the hands as they lengthen her spine.

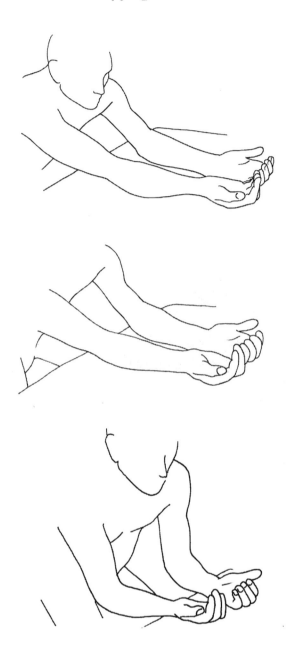

Figs. 38–40. Serpent Stretch from Above - Hand Position
The hands Bone Wash along the spine.
We can finish with the Neck Sweep, Heavens Cradle, or Opening Heaven.

The Serpent Stretch from Below

The Serpent Stretch from Below is done from a Butterfly position with our head between our partner's legs as she lays face up. When we do Serpent Stretch from Below we stretch our partner's spine in the direction of her pelvis. This position allows us to release Qi not only from most of our partner's spinal column, but also from her pelvis and legs. We can also kiss her flower as we do this.

We hook our fingers on each side of our partner's spine beginning as far up her spine as we can reach. We bring our hands toward us and when we reach her sacrum at the base of her spine we spread our hands and Bone Wash, each hand passing between her sit bone and her hip bone. We bring our hands to rest at the top of her thighs, or we can continue on, Bone Washing down her thighs.

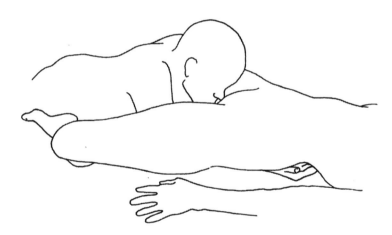

Fig. 41. Serpent Stretch from Below with Knees Down
Note hand position. The hands move down along the spine then separate along the gluts. Your partner's knees may be up or her legs can remain flat against the table. No matter the position of her legs, the movement of your hands remains the same. To release her lower back and pelvis, Bone Wash down along her spine, across her bottom, and down her legs.

Fig. 42. Serpent Stretch from Below with Knees Up
The hands in this illustration have moved from her mid to upper back
and are releasing the gluts and piriformis in her pelvis. From this position
we can also release the front, back, and sides of her thighs.

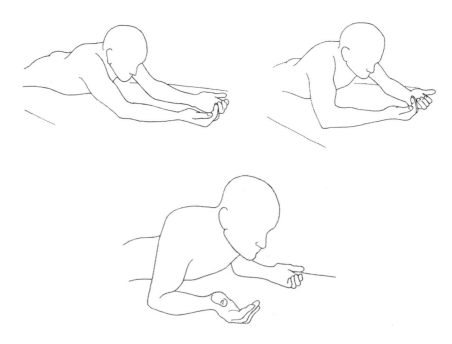

Fig. 43-45 Serpent Stretch from Below Hand Position
The hands widen around the pelvis and glide through the gluts
toward the sit bone and down the legs.

172

The Serpent Stretch from the Side

The Serpent Stretch from the Side lengthens our partner's spine toward her head while simultaneously pushing and pulling.

The Serpent Stretch from the Side is done primarily with the arm that is closest to our partner's head; the other hand is used as an anchor holding our partner's sacrum at the base of her spine. So if our partner is lying on her back, and we are standing on her right side, we use our left hand to stretch upward from her low back toward her neck and head. At the same time our right hand is between her legs reaching up toward her head and hooking her sacrum at the base of her spine. As we Bone Wash up either or both sides of her spine with our left hand we can finish the stroke by grasping and squeezing her neck and even rub her head.

If we pull our right hand out from under her bottom we will lose some leverage, but we can also use that hand to move up the front of her midline and have both hands meet at her neck.

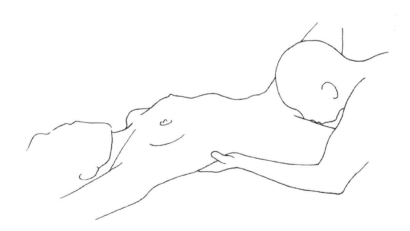

Fig. 46. Serpent Stretch from the Side
With oral stimulation

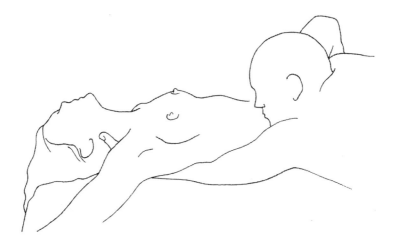

Fig. 47. Serpent Stretch from the Side
One hand Bone Washes up or down he spine while
the other cradles or pulls on the sacrum

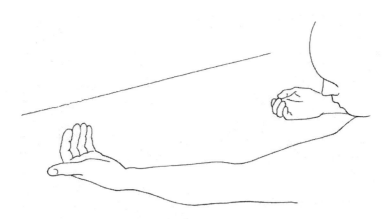

Fig. 48. Serpent Stretch from the Side Hand Positions
The right arm is between her legs, reaching up and pulling down on her
sacrum as the left hand Bone Washes up or down the spine

The Body Cradle Face Up

The Body Cradle Face Up is a modification of the Serpent Stretch from the side. As we cradle our partner we simultaneously stretch her spine with both of our hands. One arm is between her legs and the other is between her head and one of her shoulders. Our hands meet in the middle of her spine and we Bone Wash by pulling our hands apart from the middle of her spine toward the ends, fingers on each side of the spine. When the hand closer to her pelvis reaches her sacrum we can reach up and stimulate the legs of her clitoris on either side of her yoni. (See *The First Sacred Center: the Clitoris* on page 205)

From this position we can also stimulate her nipples and her flower.

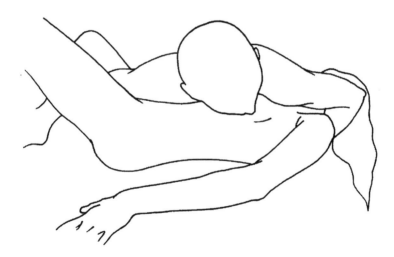

Fig. 49. Body Cradle Face Up

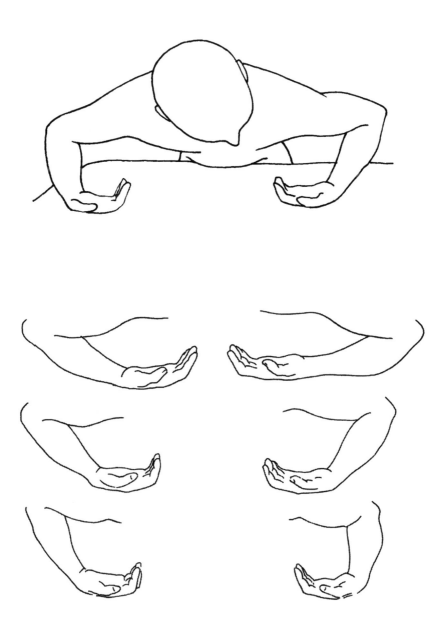

Figs. 50 & 51. Body Cradle Hand Positions
The hands move away from each other to elongate the spine.

The Body Cradle Face Down

The Body Cradle Face Down is the same as the Body Cradle Face Up except that we stimulate the ren meridian on the midline of the front of the body rather than the spine. We can also continue up the ren meridian all the way up to her throat. If the massage table she is laying on has a face cradle then it is a bit easier to access her neck as her head is face down rather than turned to one side or another.

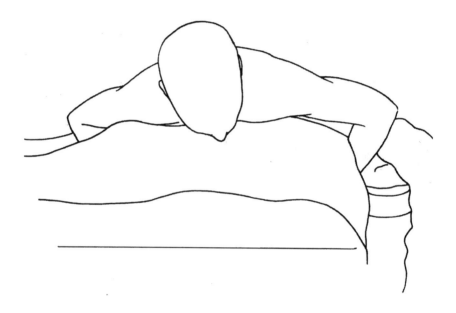

Fig. 52. Body Cradle Face Down

Opening the Armpits

The Qi in the body tends to accumulate in certain areas, most notably the neck, shoulders and upper back; the genital area and upper thighs; the area just below the rear portion of the head where the skull meets the neck, and the armpits. In Qigong the shoulder blades are kept forward the armpits are kept open in order to facilitate the flow of Qi from the lower body to the upper body. The Qi will flow more easily when the arms are kept slightly away from the body rather than pressed up against the ribcage.

So, while it is not always aesthetic or convenient to keep the arms slightly away from the body while making love, we can enhance this energetic flow by paying particular attention to our lover's ribcage and armpit area. We can (assuming she has bathed) lick, stroke, and massage this area as well as the ribcage in general, especially on the side of the body. As the first point on the heart meridian is in the armpit, this will help facilitate the full movement of Qi, and pleasure, in her body.

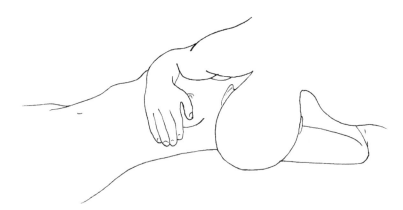

Fig. 53. Opening the Armpits

Communion

PREPARING OUR BODY

B efore we worship, we cleanse ourselves. *Our fingernails are clipped very short.* We shower or bathe, trim those nails, brush and floss. If we shave, we pay particular attention to our chin and the area around the lips. It's worth it to spend more money on quality razors. We shave as close as we can without giving ourselves a rash or cutting ourselves. If we have a beard, we wash our face.

If we use anything scented on our body we make absolutely sure that our partner does not have chemical sensitivities. We try to choose a deodorant that smells like nothing. If our deodorant does have an odor, we choose one that smells better than body odor. If in doubt, we don't use anything scented on our body.

If we are doing a Rivers of Love session we should dress in things that are pleasing to touch. Clothing should be cool, comfortable, flattering, and easy to remove. Thai fisherman pants work well, or yoga pants.

We can also ask our partner what kind of things she likes us to wear. Women pay closer attention to clothing than men. We find out what she likes.

A civil engineer must have designed the human body. Who else would run a sanitary line through a recreation area?

<small>UNKNOWN</small>

Those Dark Scary Places below the Waist

In the best of all possible worlds we would be completely comfortable with all the parts of our body and those of our partner. Given, as this is not always the case, we can still try to overcome our reticence and squeamishness. We can do our best to relax when we are worshipping the lower half of our partner. The more our partner sees us as relaxed and enjoying pleasing her, the more she will relax and be pleased.

Many women have a deeply ingrained fear that their yonis are "dirty" or that they "smell bad". If we want our partner to blossom sexually, we're going to have to let her see that we are comfortable when we are worshipping. And if we think that her flower is beautiful we should definitely tell her. A small hand held mirror can also help our partner heal from the shame that our society has placed on women, particularly around sexuality. We can hold the mirror in such a way that she can see her flower as we worship her. We can show her what we are doing and which parts we like best. We can also hold a mirror for her when she is worshipping us, so that she can see her beauty through our eyes.

If we have an aversion to bodily fluids we need to address this. Sometimes familiarity and patience will be enough to allow us to get over our aversion. If we cannot get comfortable with certain things, then ultimately we should not do them, as sexuality should always involve mutual pleasure to varying degrees.

Occasionally, if our partner really does smell ripe we might suggest taking our activities into the shower or a romantic bath and continuing our adventures in there. Creativity can work wonders here to help our partner avoid shame. Shame and nourishing sexuality are mutually exclusive.

Not all women like the same things. Some want to explore and others are more conservative. Some women enjoy having their anus stimulated. If we are pleasuring our partner's anus, we must be sure that we do not allow any part that has been in there to touch her vagina. Vigilance is required. Soap and water are a must when we are done or when we again wish to make contact with her vagina, in order to prevent infection.

Fantasy and Erotic Immersion

While making love we will often fantasize and/or deeply focus on the sensations in our own body. This is called "erotic immersion" or "sensate focus". Erotic immersion is essentially myopic. It is sex with blinders on. Like the blinders that are used on horses to keep them from being distracted, erotic immersion shuts our partner out to keep her from distracting us from our pleasurable fantasy.

In erotic immersion we are in a trance. We shut our partner out of our awareness in order to immerse ourselves in sexual pleasure. With our eyes closed we swim in a pool of erotic bliss allowing our physical sensations to increase until we climax. This can be extremely pleasurable. There is nothing wrong with erotic immersion; it is a natural part of having a healthy and viable sex life. But when we do it we are using our partner to masturbate. Masturbation is fine, but it can also be limiting. Erotic immersion, while sometimes increasing our access to pleasure, can insulate us from our partner and from true sexual intimacy. It can give us powerful orgasms, but it is not communion because when we climax we are climaxing alone.

In communion we are not blocking our partner out of our awareness to feel pleasure; we are opening to them to feel pleasure. Our focus is on what is shared, what flows between us. So erotic immersion is just one facet of many on the jewel of our lovemaking, but it should not be the only one. We should definitely add communion as another facet of our jewel. When we only have one speed, one channel, we limit ourselves. The more sensual-erotic modes in which we are fluent and comfortable, the richer will be our emotional repertoire and our love life. An effective way to move from erotic immersion to erotic communion is to learn to make love with our eyes open.

Eyes Open: To See and Be Seen

Making love with our eyes open allows us to *see* and *be seen*. In some ways this can be the ultimate mirror in our relationship.

Psychologically, opening our eyes allows us to hold space both for ourselves and for our lovemaking. When we stare at our partner we have nowhere to hide. With open eyes we cannot hide in our sexual fantasies or the titillation of our shadow. To open to a partner while climaxing can be frightening, but it can also be deeply rewarding.

Opening our eyes while making love also allows for numerous energetic possibilities. From the perspective of Chinese medicine our Shen Spirit (mind) opens from the heart and shines through the eyes. When we raise our fiery erotic energy up our spine (as in Small Heavenly Circuit) while making love, we bring our Jing Essence up to enhance the illumination of our Shen Spirit.

From a more Western perspective, we can use eye gazing as a way to connect with the erotic magnetism in all life. This was called magnetation by John William Lloyd, one of the founders of the prosexual Karezza movement of the 19th century.

John Lloyd referenced the ubiquity of life to demonstrate that sexuality is everywhere and always around us; we only need to plug into it. The planet is covered with DNA that is continually reproducing. Our bodies are covered with bacteria that are continually reproducing. The cells in our bodies are continually reproducing. The plants outside our window are reproducing. This is the ground of existence from which our species emerged. We exist in an erotic electromagnetic ocean that permeates our environment and our being. When we engage in eye gazing magnetation we allow the energy generated by our lovemaking to expand and link with the energy of life that embraces our planet.

Eyes Closed: Paliuli

Paliuli is a term I use to describe a practice that can help us re-absorb and re-circulate erotic energy back into our cells as we are making love. It is a practice that is done when we are close to climaxing, or at least in highly aroused states.

Paliuli is similar to Small Heavenly Circuit in that it can redistribute the erotic energy in our body generated by our cultivation. But it is also very different from Small Heavenly Circuit. While Small Heavenly Circuit is an active practice, Paliuli is a passive one. Small Heavenly Circuit is a channeling of energy, while Paliuli involves physical relaxation and the perfusion of that energy.

This is a very relaxed and languid practice … when we do it we are purposely creating a "wave collapse" of the intense polarity of our pre-orgasmic state. This can allow us to enter a more yin (absorbing/regenerative) state from which we can again (if we choose) build into renewed polarity with our partner.

When we move into Paliuli we close our eyes and *completely* relax our muscles, *especially* those of the head, jaw, and neck. It is also important for our spine to be long and for the back of our neck to be flat. Our ability to move into Paliuli can be enhanced on the position of our body as we are making love; we need to be completely limp and comfortable as we allow the erotic energy to permeate our cells.

The most important part of moving into Paliuli, however, is the *relaxation of our eyes and jaw*. Our eyes are closed, and as we float in our hyper-aroused state we relax our face, neck, *jaw, and eyeballs*. Of course, our whole body is relaxed, but the relaxation is centered in the back of the eyes and then ripples outward through the muscles of our body.

Our partner may not be comfortable if we move into Paliuli as we are lying on top of her (as in a Dragon position) unless she can fully support our limp weight. So, each partner can move into Paliuli one at a time, taking turns. Or we can find a side-by-side position that will allow us both full erotic polarity and the ability to completely relax our musculature on very short notice. An Infinite Touch (see page 204) or Mountain Valley (see page 204) position can work well.

Although our eyes are closed when we move into Paliuli, it should not be mistaken for fantasizing or Erotic Immersion.

As we move into Paliuli we may lose our erection. If we wish to resume polarity with our partner and continue to make love, we may also want to learn how to do Fire and Water. (See below)

Paliuli is a very nourishing practice, but it can also put us into a state of deep relaxation and sleep, so if we wish to continue love-making we may want to move into Paliuli toward the end of our session.

Paliuli can also add a very nice sense of completion as we are finishing an Erotic Will lovemaking session, but can also be done on its own whenever we like. (See Erotic Will on page 195)

Soft Entry: To Go In Like a Lamb and Come Out Like a Lion

A typical Western approach to sex extols us as men to "go in hard and come out soft". We are encouraged to be like the month of March: To go in like a lion and come out like a lamb. By contrast, in the Daoist approach the exact opposite is true. The Daoist ideal is to "go in soft and come out hard"; or we might say that we "go in like a lamb and come out like a lion".

In order to "go in soft and come out hard" we need to know how to do a soft entry with our partner.

To do a soft entry we grasp our penis by its base and wrap our fingers around it. We squeeze outward toward the tip pressing blood into the head. With the head enlarged we press it into our partner's yoni, which must be well lubricated. If done correctly we can insert our penis into her. With our soft penis snugly within our lover's yoni, we can remain in this flaccid state and practice Wei Wu Wei; or we can be more directive and use the energetic practice called Fire and Water.

Fire and Water

After we have done a soft entry and are inside our partner we can engage in what is called Fire and Water. In Fire and Water look into

Fire easily flares up but is easily extinguished by water; water takes a long time to heat over the fire, but cools down very slowly.

I CHING

our partner's eyes and we experience the energetic *pull* of her vagina. We visualize or imagine her vagina pulling our penis into her while staring into her eyes. We can directly experience the erotic tension created as the energetic polarity between the essence of her femininity, her vagina, and the essence of our masculinity, our penis, are together. As we feel her pull us and draw us into her, we will often become aroused. As our Fire becomes attracted to her Water we can let this tension build between us.

Another way to play with Fire and Water is to just let the tip of our penis enter her and allow just the head to feel the powerful pull of her primordial feminine water. As we become erect it allows her to pull us in even more.

Cultivating

Many men feel that if they do not ejaculate while making love that they might as well not have bothered making love in the first place. While this is a common feeling, our relationship to climax as men is very subjective. Although the drive to climax is innate, what we choose to do with that drive may be learned. To some men climaxing is extremely important, while to others it is not important at all.

A Daoist approach to sex focuses on the retention of semen for men. In classical Daoist thinking, semen is called Jing Essence, and is arguably the most important factor in longevity. Daoist practitioners throughout history have withheld ejaculation in order to increase their health and lifespan. The Daoists refer to this retention and recirculation of sexual energy as "cultivation".

When we cultivate, we make love or masturbate without ejaculating. But cultivation is more than simply not ejaculating. Cultivation involves moving the stored energy with our breath, refining it, and storing it for future use. Dual cultivation is when we cultivate with a partner, i.e., we are both doing cultivation practices, regardless of whether she climaxes or not.

Either you control sex or sex controls you.

DAOIST SAYING

When we cultivate what we are cultivating is life essence. When we cultivate we are "charging our battery", so to speak. Cultivation is what we do in order to build life force. When we cultivate we increase our life force in a fundamental way for our partner and ourselves. This need not be validated by "science" in order for us to do this, any more than we need to see a scientific study that validates hugging those we love. We can observe it observed amongst ourselves. The mechanisms of cultivation are vast and have been validated by many thousands of years and many thousands of Daoists. Eventually science may show that Daoist cultivation in highly aroused states activates the brain stem and the creation of stem cells. But for the time being, we can just enjoy the process and share it with our partner.

Orgasm without Ejaculation

Orgasm and ejaculation are triggered by different parts of our nervous system. While we are accustomed to experiencing them together this need not always be the case. There are men with complete high spinal cord injury that get erections and ejaculate with no orgasm whatsoever. They have to feel with their hand or look to see if they have ejaculated.

It is possible for normal healthy men to experience orgasm without ejaculation just as it is possible for us to experience ejaculation without orgasm. We may have had the experience of ejaculating with little or no orgasm. We can also learn to climax without ejaculating. While it can be a long learning curve it is possible. There are numerous books and websites out there dedicated to this practice.

There are other ways of separating ejaculation from orgasm such as pressing on the "million dollar point". The "million dollar point", described in some modern texts, is at *acupoint huiyin/ren 1*, between the testicles and the anus.

Some Daoist practices use the point *to bring one back* from the inevitability of ejaculation. Other practices involve pressing the point *in order to prevent* semen from emerging during ejaculation. This second practice can force the semen back up through the prostate and into the bladder. For health reasons *I do not recommend doing the second practice.*

Not Letting the Qi enter the Penis

If we are to refrain from ejaculating we must take care not to cause stagnation in our system or create prostate problems. This is especially true if we repeatedly bring ourselves close to climax and then back off. There is a point during sexual activity in which sperm enters the seminal vestibule and the prostate gland swells with fluid. The old Daoists say that we should not "let the Qi enter the penis", meaning that we should refrain from getting too close to climaxing but should still keep our erection. The sensation of the "Qi entering the penis" is very specific and if we pay attention we can attune ourselves to this.

If we do have the habit of "brinksmanship" or "orgasm hovering" it can put a significant amount of pressure and stress on our prostate. In order to counteract this we should do prostate massage on ourselves or have our partner do it for us.

Prostate Massage

Learning to massage our own prostate is an essential part of our reclaiming the lower half of our bodies. Taking care of our prostate is just as important as any other part of our healthcare maintenance. Massaging our prostate serves two functions. It keeps Qi and blood flowing through the area and it alerts us if there is swelling or abnormal lumps in or around our prostate.

If we repeatedly hover near orgasm we should do prostate massage on ourselves after every encounter. This will keep the blood and lymph flowing through the prostate and may help keep it from becoming hypertrophied (swollen). If we do not practice brinksmanship or are not sexually active (including masturbation) we should do prostate massage once a week. This will also keep blood and lymph flowing through the tissue. And if we are over age forty we should do prostate massage at least once per month no matter what our level of sexual activity. We do this to check for lumps and growths the same way a woman would do a breast check every month.

The easiest way to do prostate massage on ourselves is to keep some vegetable oil in the shower. Be sure that the oil is not rancid. We can put some oil on a finger and (carefully, I trust) insert it into our rectum up to the middle knuckle. We pull forward and we will be able to feel our prostate, about the size of a walnut, through the wall of our rectum. We will know that we are feeling it because we will feel a sensation of pressure in our penis when we pull forward. After pulling forward (the Daoists say nine times) we can clean up thoroughly with soap and water.

If we are checking to see if we have any prostatic enlargement or growths we can go to our doctor first and have him or her check our prostate for us so that we can get a sense of our "baseline". From that baseline we will know what is "normal" and thus if there are any changes that take place we can immediately go see our primary healthcare provider.

The perineum lift in Small Heavenly Circuit can also help to keep our prostate healthy, as will "scissoring" our legs back and forth while in a shoulder stand.

The Clouds, the Rain, and our Goddess

In Japanese culture, orgasm is sometimes referred to as "the Clouds and the Rain". There is much controversy regarding the role of women's climax in terms of longevity and the cultivation of Jing Essence.

Women have Jing Essence just as men do but they are not thought to lose their Jing through climaxing. In the Daoist classics it states that a woman's Yin is "inexhaustible", meaning that women can climax without depleting their Jing Essence. From a traditional perspective, women are thought to lose their life force more from menstruating than from climaxing.

My observation is that women may become depleted through too much climaxing, although it is not nearly as common as in men. We can ask our partner to pay attention to her physical health and her moods if she climaxes frequently and to see if she notices any difference. We, and She, can modulate our behavior accordingly.

Sexual Boredom

When we are bored with our partner, when our sex life has grown stale, the solution is not pornography or lingerie or latex sex toys. The solution is intimacy. Better visuals or stronger orgasms will not solve the problem. Sexual issues are often the manifestation of larger issues within the relationship. If our relationship is a yoga or a path, then deepening the emotional honesty with our partner will often deepen our love life, but only if we are rooted in ourselves. If we have not rooted in ourselves the deepening intimacy may drive us away.

We may then think that a new lover will solve our problem of boredom. Often it will, until our new lover becomes boring. Then we repeat the pattern, looking for yet another lover. After a while our lives can seem like Bill Murray's in the movie *Groundhog Day*. Granted, an endless stream of lovers may seem like an appealing fantasy. But after a while it invariably becomes empty, our lovers become cartoons, and we move and speak as if on autopilot. Our glandular self-medication strategies no longer work. We find ourselves doing it more but enjoying it less and less.

Some of this is biological in us as men. We are aroused by variety. Still, if we do not cultivate our ability to be intimate, we severely limit our erotic potential. How long can we avoid intimacy and still expect to have fulfilling relationships?

We may just be bored from being with the same partner. But if this "boredom" is really a fear of intimacy, then we are deluding ourselves. If we do not have the courage to address that fear, we deny our partner, and ourselves, the opportunity to embrace who we are at depth.

Ejaculation Control

One of the great gifts that we can give to our partner is our ability to choose when we are going to ejaculate. In order to hold space while making love we must allow enough time for us to reach communion with our partner, and ultimately transcendence. As a man, we must delay our gratification and refrain from ejaculating. In some ways keeping our Jing Essence inside us is similar to what we do when we root in ourselves. In both cases we need to pay attention to what is going on in us, we cannot go unconscious or be pulled off balance due to outside influences. If we are making love we cannot go into erotic immersion. When we pay attention to ourselves we deepen our inner awareness, creating pathways within us that lead to our core.

Ejaculation control is learned, and it is learned through practice, although it becomes easier as we age. . Premature ejaculation is often caused by tension and performance anxiety, but there are other reasons also. Sometimes we are not aware when we are about to climax so we do not know when it is time to slow down. We can do some practices on our own, without our partner. We can learn to recognize when we are near threshold by masturbating but not allowing ourselves to ejaculate. We can learn where our edge is. If we watch our own reactions carefully we will begin to see stages of arousal that previously were just a blur. Although ejaculation control is important, detailed information on how to do this is beyond the scope of this book.

There can be back of the neck orgasms, bottom of the foot orgasms, and palm of the hand orgasms.

MASTERS AND JOHNSON

I want to stay as close to the edge as I can without going over. Out on the edge you see all kinds of things you can't see from the center.

KURT VONNEGUT

Condoms

Condoms suck, but they do not suck nearly as much as a sexually transmitted disease. When we use a condom we still have 99% of our bodies through which we can exchange energy. Qi runs everywhere. Qi runs throughout us and we can exalt in its power. We can learn to transmit and receive Qi with the other 99% of our body.

Erotic Will

We can use the Qi and Jing Essence that is generated during intense sexual experiences to align our unconscious mind with a desired outcome. To do this we link two things together in our nervous system. This is called *anchoring*. In Chinese medicine this anchoring of our mind to an outcome is called the Zhi (will) and is ruled by the kidneys. If we repeatedly anchor a desired outcome to an intense pre-orgasmic experience, our unconscious mind will soon associate that outcome with a hunger for intense pleasure. It does not take long to condition this response. When that happens the unconscious mind begins to align itself in the world and generate behaviors in us that help to create this outcome. Our unconscious helps us say and do things that help the outcome to manifest. When our unconscious is aligned and anchored to an intention we magnetize our lives. Through subtle cues we magnetize anyone near us to help us create what we want.

If we are in our Erotic Will with a partner who is not doing it with us, that is fine. It is more powerful if two people do it together but it is not necessary to have both of us practicing for it to be effective.

We set the intention of our Will before we make physical contact with our partner. We allow our touch as it flows over our partner's body to clarify and "charge" the intention of our Will. As we make love the friction generated by our genitals creates heat. This heat builds and we can magnify and move it, allowing it to permeate different parts of our body. As we find ourselves becoming more aroused, we activate Small Heavenly Circuit. When we feel significant Qi and Jing

To me inspiration and creativity come only when I have abstained from a woman for a longish period. When, with passion, I have emptied my fluid into a woman until I am pumped dry, then inspiration shuns me. The same forces which go to fertilize a woman and create a human being go to create a work of art.

FREDERIC CHOPIN

Essence building, we bring it up the spine and let it fill our head as if our skull was a bowl of liquid light. We keep the curve of the neck flat to allow the energy to flow. We do this three or four more times, each time allowing more and more refined light to enter our crown. As we build to a crescendo, we do not ejaculate, but rather choose a point somewhere in space that is infused with our intention, with our desired outcome. Selecting a specific star can work very well for this. Our desired outcome could be something as mundane a having more money or as altruistic as wanting peace of mind for a friend of ours. Rather than ejaculating we send all that built up energy to that tiny point filled with our intention.

Because we have not ejaculated but we have come very close, we should be sure to move Qi sometime after doing this. We can move Qi by stretching, receiving massage, or just going into a state of deep relaxation. Or we can slip into *Paliuli* (see page 183).And of course, when we are finished, prostate massage is a good idea. Our partner may also do this for us.

Positions for Communion

In describing sexual positions I have purposely avoided the common locker room vernacular usually associated with intimate practices. We need not compare our most intimate and sacred activities with debased descriptions of street mammals or sex-negative purveyors of religion. There is so much profanity in our language that infects and contaminates our sexual perceptions that I choose to not pass on that infection to my readers. Hence I have chosen not to perpetuate those terms in this book. A lot of the following terminology may be unfamiliar, but hopefully it is an improvement over what has gone before.

Lotus Position

In the Lotus position the woman sits astride the man who is sitting up cross-legged, or in a lotus or half lotus position. This position is also called Yab Yum.

Lotus position can be very heart opening between couples and can be used to generate compassion and connection. Qi Release of much of the body is also possible from this position, as are most of the dual cultivation Qigong practices.

Fig. 54. Lotus position

Phoenix Position

In the Phoenix position the woman straddles atop the man facing him as he lies on his back.

The Phoenix position is more power oriented toward the female and can facilitate the strengthening of her Shen Spirit (mind). In this position the woman can control which of her two internal sacred spots are stimulated and to what depth and strength. (See *The Three Sacred Centers and the Three Sacred Waters* on page 205.)

The woman must take care not to thrust at uncomfortable angles lest she thrust in a direction and with such intensity that she damages her partner's penis.

Either partner can release Qi from the other partner's torso from this position.

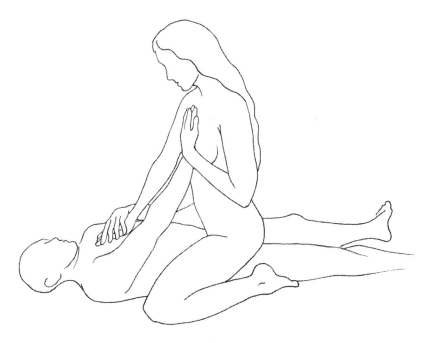

Fig. 55. Phoenix position

Dragon Position

In the Dragon position the man and the woman are laying horizontally. They face each other and the man is on top. The woman's legs are spread and the man's weight is resting on his elbows and forearms. This position is commonly referred to by a very unpleasant name.

When done with eyes open, the Dragon position can increase heart opening between couples.

This position lends itself well to the man releasing his partners neck and shoulders. From this position the woman can also Bone Wash along her partners spine.

And from a modified Dragon position the man can suck his partner's toes while making love. Considering that the part of our Goddess' brain that controls her yoni is right next to the part of her brain that controls her feet, she may find this approach particularly arousing.

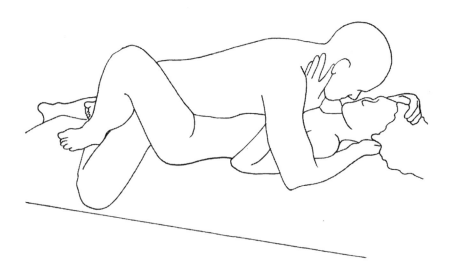

Fig. 56. Dragon position

Tiger / Leopard / Panther Positions

The Tiger position has the man on his knees behind the woman who is on all fours. Like the Dragon position, the Tiger position also has an alternative common and crude name. Other cat positions are the Leopard, in which the man is standing and the woman is bent over and the Panther in which the man is standing and the woman is lying across a table or a massage table.

The cat positions are more power oriented toward the male. As with any power, this energy must be modulated with responsibility, sensitivity, and respect. If the man is not in tune with the woman's physical or psychological comfort, he may inadvertently injure his partner's body or her Shen Spirit (mind).

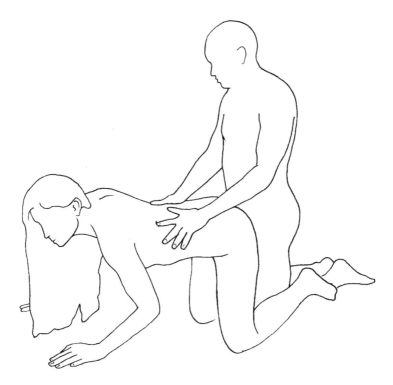

Fig. 57. Tiger position

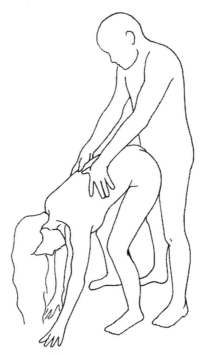

Fig. 58. Leopard position

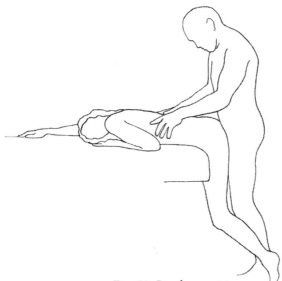

Fig. 59. Panther position

Yin Yang Position

In the Yin Yang position the couples take a "North-South" position with each person's head between the legs of the other partner.

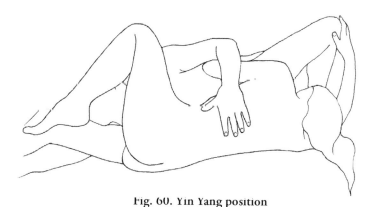

Fig. 60. Yin Yang position

Butterfly Position

The Butterfly position is also called "Drinking in the Moon Cream". In this position the woman lies on her back and the man has his head, and sometimes his hands, between her legs.

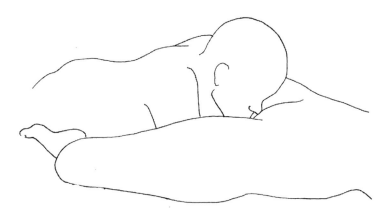

Fig. 61. Butterfly position

Mountain Valley Position

In the Mountain Valley position we are lying on our side behind our partner who is also lying on her side. Our knees are slid in behind hers.

Fig. 62. Mountain Valley position

Infinite Touch (Wei Wu Wei) Position

In our Infinite Touch position we lay side by side with our legs "scissored" between our partner's legs. The leg of our partner that is closest to us is on top, and the leg of ours that is closest to our partner is on the bottom. (See Infinite Touch page 245)

Fig. 63. Infinite Touch position

The Three Sacred Centers
and the Three Sacred Waters

Drawing Back the Curtain

We can push back our partner's *mons veneris* (the pubic mound) and *draw back the curtain* with our hand or even (if we are gentle) our upper lip as we kiss our partners clitoris.

The Three Sacred Centers and the Three Sacred Waters

Our partner has Three Sacred Centers and Three Sacred Waters within her pelvis. The First Sacred Center is the clitoris located above the vulva. The Sacred Water of the clitoris is vaginal fluid that is released during arousal and used to moisten the yoni. The Second Sacred Center is inside the vagina just behind the pubic bone. This is sometimes called the "Sacred Spot", or "G Spot". The Sacred Water of the Second Sacred Center is sometimes called "Amrita" and is secreted from the Skenes Glands (the female "prostate") during intense arousal. The Third Sacred Center is the cervix and the tissue just around it, also called the North Star or the Pole Star by the Daoists. In Chinese reflexology the cervix corresponds to the heart, which is the deepest, and most core part of one's being. The cervix is the gateway to the womb. The Sacred Water of the cervix is fluid that is released in profound emotional opening during lovemaking. I call the opening and flowering of the cervix Blooming of Plumeria. It is the one of the deepest and most intimate ways that our partner can receive us.

The First Sacred Center: the Clitoris

What we see of the clitoris from the outside is merely a small part of a much larger organ. What we think of as the clitoris is really the glans, or just the head of the clitoris. The clitoris actually has "legs" or "crura" (singular: "crus") that run along either side of the vagina, in the crease where the legs meet the pelvis. We can rub, lick, or touch these "legs" much to our partner's pleasure long before we ever touch her yoni. This is an important part of Broad Brush Qi Release in Rivers of Love. There are also two vestibular bulbs that go inside our lover's body that are also part of the clitoris. These run alongside the inside of the vagina.

It is always a good idea to go avoid going directly to the clitoris when we are worshipping our partner. It is far better to circumnavigate our favorite place on the planet for a while in order to be assured that we are well received. See *Foreplay: Circling in for a Loving Landing* (see page 149). Once she is very aroused and we move to touch our partner's First Sacred Center, the clitoris, our touch should be light, moist, smooth, and silky … the lighter the better.

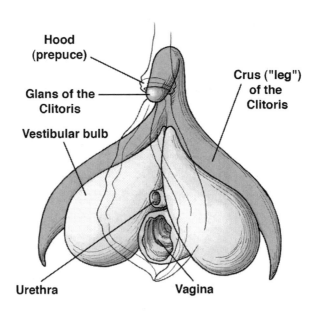

Fig. 64. The First Sacred Center: the Clitoris

I nanea no ka holo o ka wa`a i ke akamai o ke ku hoe.

One can enjoy a canoe ride

when the paddler is skilled.

Hawaiian proverb

The Second Sacred Center: the "G" Spot

We can stimulate the Second Sacred Center with our fingers or with our penis. As with her other Sacred Centers, we should wait until our partner is adequately aroused before we begin to massage her Second Sacred Center.

Her Second Sacred Center is just behind the pubic bone inside the yoni. It will feel like a small mound of raised tissue. If we insert our fingers into her flower with the palm up, and we curl our fingers back toward us, we will hit her Sacred Spot. Sometimes we can hit her Sacred Spot while making love if we are in the right position.

In a developing fetus, the cells from which her Second Sacred Center is formed are the same cells from which the prostate gland is formed in men.

The Third Sacred Center: the Cervix

As the cervix becomes stimulated it can open and energetically draw our penis toward it. Our heart center (the head of our penis) can "kiss" our partner's heart center (her cervix) creating deeper and

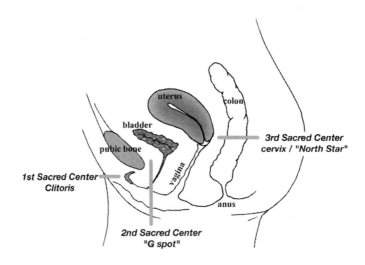

Fig. 65. The Three Sacred Centers: The Clitoris, "G" Spot, and Cervix

deeper heart openings in both partners. Continued stimulation of the cervix can result in the "Blooming of Plumeria" which can release the Third Sacred Water from our partner's yoni. Care must be taken here; stimulation that is too long or too vigorous can cause a painful spasm in her uterus. We can also use our hand to stimulate her here, gently encircling her Third Sacred Center. We should be gentle and pay attention.

Opening Her Flower

An important part of worshipping our partner is called "Opening Her Flower", in which we kiss, lick, and stimulate her yoni with our mouth and fingers. Opening Her Flower is generally done from a Butterfly position; but there are lots of other possibilities. While there are many ways to please our partner with our mouth, generally speaking the lighter and more delicate the stimulation, the better. One way of opening the flower is called Lapping Honey, or Drinking the Moon Cream. This is a *slow* and sensuous single lick with extended tongue from the bottom of the vagina all the way to above the clitoris. As we lick upward we allow our bottom lip to continue licking upward after our tongue has passed the top of the clitoris.

When we open her flower we are honoring the creation place from which all life emerges. We experience our partner as a flower that is bursting forth, ready to receive our love and adoration.

While we are worshipping, our partner may be afraid that she is unpleasant "down there" or that she smells bad. (See *Those Dark Scary Places Below the Waist* page 181 for further suggestions for dealing with this.)

Qi Communion Techniques

Qi Communion (lovemaking/bodywork) techniques are Qi Release techniques combined with genital contact. So we are doing massage and making love in one form or another.

In the Nubian language, the word for knowledge and the word that describes the female sex organs is the same word: "shi tet".

NUT TMU-ANKH BUTTERFLY

Graze on my lips; and if those be dry, Stray lower, where the pleasant fountains lie.

WILLIAM SHAKESPEARE

Qi Release from Any Position

When we are making love we can release Qi with our lover from any position. We are limited only by our reach, physical comfort, and imagination. From a Dragon position (with a bit of weight shift on an oiled massage table) we can reach our partner's front and back torso, neck and head, pelvis, and to a certain degree legs. From a Tiger position we can easily reach her spine, neck, rear pelvis, and upper legs. From a Phoenix position we can easily reach her ribcage on the front, etcetera....

In the following sections I describe some possibilities, but there are obviously many others. Please note that Rivers of Love is about pleasure, fulfillment and intimacy, not acrobatics. We should not get too hung up in intricate positions. Intimate and simple works....

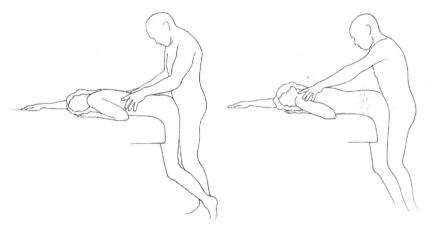

Fig. 66. Qi Release (Bone Washing) from the Panther position

Opening the Butterfly Wings

Opening the Butterfly Wings is a form of Qi release done from the Butterfly position with our head between your partner's legs. From this position we can release Qi from her adductors, hamstrings, quadriceps, gluts, quadratus, and piriformis, not to mention her lower legs and feet. We can even do limited Serpent Stretches on her spine, at least to her lower and mid back.

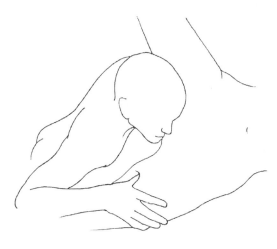

**Fig. 67. Opening the Butterfly Wings
Qi Release (Bone Washing) along the
adductors while stimulating her yoni.
Note the right thumb releasing her adductors.**

The Temple body-work (Broad Brush) Qi Release can be done while in minimally aroused states as we begin to kiss her flower. As her arousal increases we can segue into Bone Washing around her legs and pelvis, either toward or away from her genitals. We should be sure to move slowly and carefully while Bone Washing from a Butterfly position, we definitely do not want to rush. We can allow plenty of time for the tissue to release, especially on her adductors along her inner thighs and along the iliotibial band on her outer legs.

By this time we might have noticed that we can Bone Wash with one hand and we will still have five spare digits loitering nearby. Well, after our partner's heart and flower have been sufficiently opened, we may be able to find these digits gainful employment. You know what they say about "idle hands"....

Our "idle" fingers can be used to stimulate the outer labia of our partner's yoni as we arouse her with our tongue. We may also stimulate her rectally with our finger if she (and we) are so inclined. We may even (carefully and gently!) do all three simultaneously. (See *Those Dark Scary Places Below the Waist* page 181)

As she approaches climax we can begin to bone wash her legs and pelvis deeper, while still keeping our Bone Washing movement very slow and intentional.

Circle 'Round the Moon

While our partner is approaching climax we may have one hand stimulating her flower and the other Bone Washing the back of her pelvis and her thighs. At this point we can take the hand that is Bone Washing and deeply and slowly circle her ischeal tuberosity ("sit bone"), first on one side of her pelvis and then on the other. When done at the right way, during a high state of arousal, this "circling 'round the moon" can trigger global pelvic release.

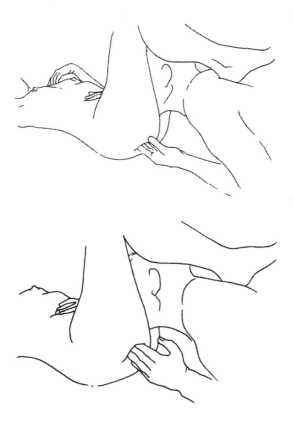

Fig. 68 / 69 Circle Round the Moon
Qi Release (Bone Washing) around the Ischeal Tuberosity (sit bone).
Note the movement of the left hand. The right hand can press on her lower abdomen toward the yoni, fingers and thumb on either side of the bladder.

Releasing the Yang Qi

The Qi in the body is separated into two types, Yin Qi and Yang Qi.

The Yin Qi in the body is more nourishing and moves deeper to nourish our internal organs. The Yang Qi in the body is more fiery and protective and tends to move to the outside and toward the head. All the Yang meridians of the body flow through the neck to the head. What we think of as stress is often this Yang Qi getting stuck in a "traffic jam" between the shoulder blades as it rises toward our head. This is the reason why many of us enjoy having our shoulders massaged when we are tense. When we release our partner's Yang Qi, we massage her shoulder blades and upper back while she is aroused. When this energy is released we may feel simultaneously relaxed and energized.

Releasing the Yang Qi is a pleasurable way to help our partner reduce stress and increase her energy. If she has been under a lot of stress lately she may not be feeling particularly sexy; so it may take a while for her to feel amorous. Before releasing the Yang Qi in a Rivers of Love session, we may want to consider other things that make her feel nourished and loved, such as gently bathing her or giving her a non-sexual but very sensual Broad Brush massage.

Now, reaching our partner's shoulder blades while sexually arousing her can be a bit of a project, depending on our position. It is easiest from a Dragon position (remember that our lover is well oiled and our hands can move beneath her) but releasing the Yang Qi while making love is often done from a Yin Yang position. It can also be done from other positions.

Our partner may be either on the top or the bottom of our Yin Yang. An advantage to having her on top is that our head is supported as we kiss her yoni. An advantage of having her on the bottom is that the weight of her body may allow us to release her upper back more thoroughly as her weight drives her muscles into our waiting fingers. If she is on the bottom, our forehead rests between her legs on the table or the bed. We kiss her yoni while our arms are between her body and the table. Our fingers are curved and we are doing Narrow Brush Qi Release around her shoulder blades.

If we do it while lying side-by-side one of our arms can become immobilized in the mix. Our lower hand can hold her thigh that is closest to the table while our uppermost hand can do Qi release along her spine. As we kiss our partner's yoni and she becomes more aroused she will allow her upper back and shoulder blades to merge into our firm fingers.

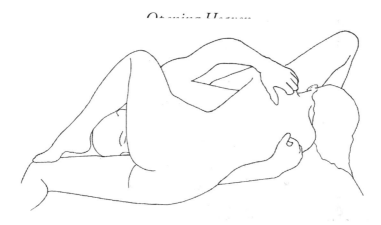

Fig. 70. Releasing the Yang Qi (Bone Washing) from the Yin Yang position
Note the hand position between the shoulder blades

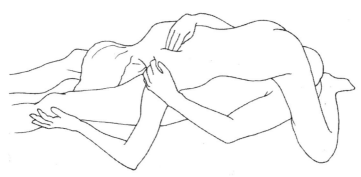

Fig. 71. Releasing the Yang Qi (Bone Washing) from the Yin Yang position
Note the hands releasing the shoulder

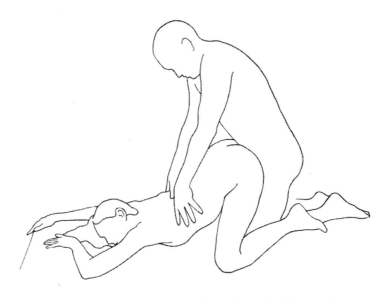

Fig. 72. Qi Release (Bone Washing) from the Tiger position
Her kidneys can be strengthened from this position and the Yang Qi
between the shoulder blades can be released.

After releasing her Yang Qi from between her shoulder blades, the Qi will tend to rise from her shoulders and move up her neck and into her head. The more aroused she becomes the more Qi she will generate and the more Qi will be released. To further facilitate this movement of energy we can massage her scalp. Massaging her scalp is called "Opening Heaven". When we Open Heaven we clear the pathway for the Qi that has moved up into her head. We can Open Heaven while making love in a Dragon or Phoenix position, or intermittently after doing a Serpent Stretch and a Neck Sweep. She may find this scalp massage very arousing, especially if we are simultaneously stimulating her yoni or sucking on her nipple. Opening Heaven is good for her in the sense that it prevents the Qi we have already released from her upper back and shoulders from again becoming stuck in her head. She will thank us for this.

SOMETHING FOR US

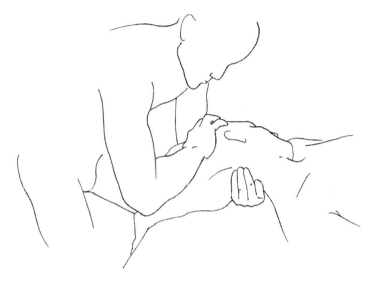

Fig. 73. Opening Heaven
Scalp massage

Drinking the Sun Essence

Our partner may want to worship our masculine energy as well, and one of the ways that she might find this most pleasurable is to honor us with her mouth. In old sacred temples this was done as a way of connecting men to the Goddess, reuniting them with the great mysteries. Women invoked Goddess energy and shared that energy in reverence with men, showering them in the power of the feminine.

There is something remarkably powerful when this energy is shared between two people who love each other. It is always pleasurable for us as men to be honored in this way, but fellatio can become energetic and transcendent when eye contact is maintained between partners and sacred space is held. Keeping eye contact allows the energy to flow much more easily both in our partner and us. With the power of her erotic body and the focus of her eyes she can chan-

Have you swallowed your husband's semen in the hope that because of your diabolical deed he might burn all the more with love and desire for you? If you have done this you should do penance for seven years on legitimate holy days.

BURCHARD, 10TH CENTURY ROMAN CATHOLIC BISHOP

nel the deep mystery of Goddess energy. She can exalt and humble us. Her eyes can arouse. They can sparkle and shimmer. She can draw our energy down into her dan tian (abdomen) through her mouth and then send it up her spine and back out to us through her eyes.

There is so much pornography showing women giving men oral sex while being demeaned that our paradigms have become desecrated, our love has been reduced to a foul cartoon. It is important to tell our partner how beautiful she is as she honors us so that she (and we) can experience this honoring as the energetic pinnacle that it is. We should understand this as an expression of love and sharing of pleasure and reinforce this perception so that our partner does not become shamed by common and base cultural misperceptions.

When a woman honors us with her mouth she can also suck on us in a way that pleases *her*. (See *Touching to Receive* page 154) This is very different than the way she might normally have us in her mouth, using her mouth and tongue to try to please *us*. She can use the sensations of us in her mouth to pleasure herself. She can run us along the insides of her cheeks, caress her lips, and otherwise sensually explore us in a way that she finds arousing. This can shift and empower her relationship with our penis, and can ultimately help her discover her own potency and ability to be aroused. There are certain esoteric traditional Daoist practices in which women use specific fellatio techniques to preserve their beauty and increase longevity.

Contempt of sexuality is a crime against life.

FRIEDRICH NIETZSCHE

Ritual

Introduction to Ritual

The Importance of Ritual

The word "ritual" can mean different things. It can refer to our daily "rituals" of showering, shaving and eating breakfast. These are rituals, but these not the types of rituals that we're concerned with here.

In our modern world of technological materialism and our break-neck pace of life we have lost the life-affirming power of ritual. Hell, in our madness we have lost the life-affirming power of *anything*.

What I refer to as ritual is behavior that frames and embodies the sacred. This is "consecration", our art of creating the sacred. To participate in ritual is to consecrate intention of the Will.

If we want to reclaim our life and our love we will need to slow down. Ritual decelerates us to a pace from which we can focus our intention while infusing our interactions with meaning.

Ritual, by its nature connects us to the sacred. It is the outer manifestation of a deep and profound inner process. We use ritual to simultaneously engage outer and inner worlds. A ritual need not be routine or rehearsed; it can be quite spontaneous. Ritual can be physical, emotional, energetic, spiritual, or all of the above. Ritual can mean the difference between a great sexual encounter and a mind blowing one.

PREPARING THE SPACE

When we prepare space, we create sacred space. When we hold space we hold sacred space. In Rivers of Love we want our sacred space to engage all of our partner's senses in as many ways as we can imagine.

Turn off the cat and put out the phone. Draw the door and lock the curtains.

Sight: dimmed light, soft and sensual colors.

Sound: repetitive soothing music will work. If we are being particularly wild and edgy, we can play music that is more intense, driving and primal, but this might not lend itself to ritual. Or perhaps it might. Let me know what you've figured out.

Smell: essential oils, flowers, scented oil, etc. cinnamon oil. Lemon oil. Again, we should be sure that our partner does not have chemical sensitivities.

Taste: chocolate, fruit, powdered sugar, chocolate, honey, ice cream, ice cubes, chocolate.

Touch: Heated oil for bodywork and possibly for personal lubricant. If not oil then we can use another personal lubricant. Fabrics such as cotton, flannel, silk, or satin work well. Birth control, if needed, is kept nearby.

Other: Dry towels, bathrobe or sarong. Heated moist towels are perfect to wipe down our partner's body after a session. She will be grateful.

Clearing the Space

When we clear space we "wipe the board clean" so to speak. We may cleanse the room, the table, our partner, or ourselves. We may cleanse any of these, mentally or physically. We remove distractions, obstructions, and obstacles that prevent us from focusing or our partner from experiencing energetic and erotic flow.

We can clear a space by literally cleaning the room in which the ritual is to take place: mopping, sweeping, washing linens, etc. We make sure that we have what we are going to need ahead of time so that we don't have to go looking for things during the ritual.

But we can also clear the space in an energetic way. We clear space as a prelude to consecration. We energetically wipe everything clean before setting an intention. Almost all spiritual traditions have rituals to clear areas. Different traditions do this in different ways. A simple way is to imagine a clear white light purifying everything in the room. If we want to we can pray out loud or intone. Tibetan bells, bowls, or incense may be used. Salt is a universal purifier for sacred space, as is consecrated water. Plants are often used. Native Americans use sage and Hawaiians use la'i (*Cordyline terminalis*)

Consecration (Setting Intention)

After we have wiped the board clean, so to speak, we may wish to write something upon it. Before we "write" we should carefully consider what we wish to create with this session, i.e., what we wish to "write". In setting intention we energetically focus on a desired outcome.

When we consecrate a room, a body, or a ritual we create sacred intentional space in ourselves and/or our environment. When we consecrate before a Rivers of Love session, we infuse sacred energy and *intention* into the room, the table, our partner's body and spirit, and our own body and spirit.

The heights of sex stir us to quickly remove
the clothes of our lovers before having sex.
The depths of sacred sex encourage us
to dress them afterwards.

MICHAEL MIRDAD

In the physical realm we set intention in a Rivers of Love ritual by using the oil brush to draw words or symbols on the massage table or vinyl covered bed. We may paint images, glyphs, symbols, Chinese characters, or words that represent our intention for that session. We do this and our partner does also. Then we smooth out the words and symbols to cover the surface with oil.

In the mental or energetic realm we set intention by aligning our unconscious mind with the task at hand and creating congruence between our thoughts, intentions and behaviors. We do this by visualizing outcomes. We may visualize our partner and ourselves as having abundant energy, clear and healthy skin tone, emotional resonance, or any other desired outcome. After this initial visualization is done, we can forget about it, allowing our unconscious mind to do that work as our conscious mind focuses on our partner's pleasure.

When we align our conscious intention with ritual to help engage our unconscious mind and combine them with states of high arousal and deep tissue bodywork, powerful experiences can emerge.

A RIVERS OF LOVE RITUAL

A Rivers of Love Communion session emerges in stages or phases. We have delineated these steps only as an example of what is possible for a couple to create. These steps are not written in stone and you can change their order; mix and match them as you please. Feel free to omit any part that does not work for both of you.

These are steps that we have found to work.

Please note that these steps are for us as *man* doing this ritual for a *woman*. The ritual for *her* doing this for *us* is somewhat different and accommodates some of the structural and energetic differences between men and women. The ritual for a woman honoring a man will be described in the upcoming book *"Rivers of Love: Sexuality in the Heart of Healing"*.

1) Cleansing Ourselves

2) Clearing and Consecrating the Room

3) Setting Intention on the Massage Table or Bed.

4) Consecrating the Beloved—Prayer or Meditation

5) Anointing the Beloved

6) Qi Release Temple Bodywork

7) Qi Release Bone Washing

8) Single or Dual Cultivation Qigong

9) Resolution

> Draining Excess Qi
> Returning the Qi to the Source
> Coming to Completion
> Prayer
> Mountain Valley
> Check In

10) Bathing the Goddess

Cleansing Ourselves

We bathe ourselves. If we wish we can also bathe our partner. At this point we can also heat the oil to be ready when we set intention on the table and warm some towels to wipe the oil off our partner when the session is done.

Clearing and Consecrating the Room

The Clearing and Consecration can be done while our partner is in the room or while she is bathing. If she is in the room we should be sure that she is warm enough.

The room can be "cleared" by doing a cleansing ritual or by visualizing it being filled with a bright white light. We can use Tibetan singing bowels or anything else we want to enhance the experience.

After "clearing", we consecrate the room by setting a direct intention for it, as if the room itself were a living being that had a vital function in the Rivers of Love session. We give it the function of holding space, just as we will hold space for our partner in this session. We can do this by visualizing our intention permeating the room, penetrating into every corner and even into the walls.

Setting Intention on the Massage Table or Bed

Using a Sumi paintbrush and warmed oil, we consecrate the table by using warm oil to paint words, symbols or designs on it. Our partner can do this with us, or we can prepare the table as she watches. When we have completed the painting, our partner and we can spread the oil across the table with our hands, energizing the table with our mutual intention.

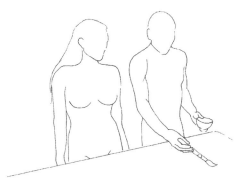

Fig. 74 / 75 Setting Intention on the
Massage Table
Painting symbols or words with oil on
the massage table

Consecrating the Beloved—Prayer or Meditation

When we consecrate the Beloved we bless her. We set our intention for her wellbeing and for her experience at the outcome of this session.

We have our partner lie naked face down on a massage table or a piece of vinyl spread out on the bed. Again, make sure that the room is warm enough for her. If it is not, we may want to drape her with something. We place one hand on her heart area on her mid back on her heart and one hand on her sacrum (below her low back at the high point of her pelvis).

We can pray, chant, tone, visualize, or meditate, whatever we are comfortable with.

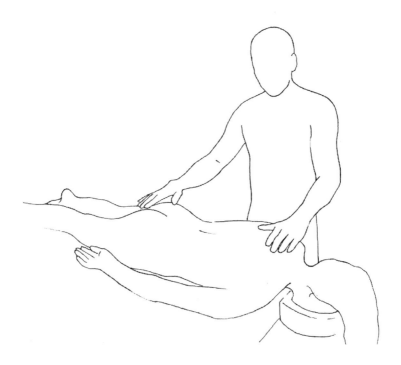

Fig. 76. Consecrating the Beloved

Anointing the Beloved

Before beginning her anointing we can also paint consecration characters or symbols on her back. After we do this we can then go ahead and anoint her.

Fig. 77. Anointing the Beloved

Using the Sumi brush and a bowl of warmed oil, we softly paint the oil on her body beginning at her right shoulder and moving in a clockwise direction, down her arm across her fingers. We take our time. We gently lubricate her armpit and the upper part of her torso where it meets the table. We move across her buttocks and down her right leg, spending time on her feet and toes. We move up her left leg, taking care to gently lubricate her inner legs and thighs with the

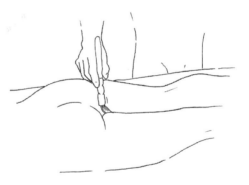

Fig. 78. Anointing the Beloved

brush. We can drizzle oil above her yoni and along her inner thighs, and then gently stroke her yoni with the brush. Please note that if her yoni is sensitive we may not be able to use oil as a lubricant. We continue on to her left buttocks and on to her left hand, up her left arm, armpit and along the left side of her torso. Finally we oil her neck and back.

It may take some practice to determine the amount of oil that works best.

Qi Release (Broad Brush) Temple Bodywork

After we have anointed our partner, we can begin anywhere, remembering to Circle in for a Loving Landing. (See page 149) We can begin by working along her spine or anywhere that we think she might enjoy. We keep our movements smooth and fluid, using our forearms and even our torso along the full length of her body. We can begin to slide our hands and forearms under her body, being sure to thoroughly stimulate her arms, legs and abdomen. We should not forget her fingers and toes as these hold very powerful acupuncture points. We can suck and lick them as well as massaging them. We should move slowly and deliberately.

As we see our partner's breath begin to deepen we can begin massaging her breasts. We should pay particular attention to the breasts, lingering for quite a while. If she is large breasted we should make sure that there is enough oil on the table. We can then increase the length of our strokes to include her abdomen, thighs and even neck if we can reach it from underneath her body. We can spend some time lingering under her arms and on the sides of her ribcage.

As her arousal increases even more we can begin massaging her inner thighs while periodically moving up and down her torso. We should remember to hold space and *take our time*. This is for her pleasure before it is for ours. At another time, when she is worshipping us, we can receive pleasure just for ourselves. Slowly we move closer and closer toward her yoni, running our hands up along her inner thighs but never directly touching her flower. Because the legs of the clitoris run along the crease where the leg meets the groin, we are actually stimulating her clitoris by doing this. *Up to this point we have not directly touched our partner's yoni or the head of her clitoris.* We can continue by doing a body cradle; one arm is stretched up between her legs and moves up her belly toward her breasts. The other comes down from above either shoulder, between her breasts. Both arms are between her body and the table, and the hands can move toward each other. We can also move from the side of her body rather than the shoulder and connect along the side of the torso, cradling one side of her pelvis.

Now we ask her to turn over, if she is on a massage table we remove the face cradle. We want to keep her aroused as we work her spine and neck, so we can kiss and suck her breasts as our hands work on her spine and neck.

By this point she may be very aroused. Once she is significantly aroused we can begin bone washing.

Qi Release (Narrow Brush) Bone Washing

We can really get creative with our partner at this point, beginning to tighten our circles as we start approaching for a loving landing. Even as we are getting closer to her yoni, we still want to periodically move back toward the periphery to keep it interesting and keep her whole body illuminated.

When she is highly aroused we can initiate any of the Qi release techniques or Qi communion techniques that have previously covered. We have gone over Qi release techniques from numerous positions but we are limited only by our imagination.

Communion: Single or Dual Cultivation Qigong

We can do our own Qigong while doing bodywork on our partner. It also may be possible that she may wish us to coach her in her Qigong breathing while we are doing Qi release, opening her flower, or possibly even penetrating her. If she is open to being coached, so much the better. If not, we should not force the issue.

We can also do dual cultivation with her, including Qigong partner techniques such as Small Heavenly Circuit for Two or Ribbon Breathing. We can even do Erotic Will together. (See page 195)

If our Qigong is automatic and has become an intuitive part of our muscle memory, we can continue to do Bone Washing on her as we practice Qigong.

Resolution

Draining Excess Qi

When we are ready to conclude the session, we can begin the resolution phase of the ritual. We should confirm with her that she is ready to draw the session to a close.

Standing next to the table we take our hands and begin to drain excess Qi from her body. First we squeeze her arms, rubbing and twisting down toward her fingers, neglecting neither the fingers nor the fingertips. Then we squeeze her legs, one at a time, with a lot of strength, draining her excess Qi. It is as if we were trying to milk the excess Qi that has been created and drain it from her body. We start at the top of her legs and one at a time, use our hands to squeeze each leg toward the toes. We should be sure to drain her legs completely, although care should be taken behind the knee and around the ankles so as not to hurt her. This squeezing should continue out through the tips of her toes.

Returning the Qi to the Source

At this point we can take her hands in ours and coach her in *putting her Qi away*. We take her hands and have her circle her lower abdomen (dan tian). This returns the Qi in the body to its source.

Coming to Completion (Prayer)

We then take one hand and place it on her heart and the other hand and place it very firmly on her pubic mound and covering her yoni completely. We can then do a prayer, invocation, or meditation.

Mountain Valley

Getting back on the table, we can go into a Mountain Valley position with her head resting on our upper arm that is closest to the table, and our other arm is wrapped around her torso with one hand resting on her heart. (See page 204)

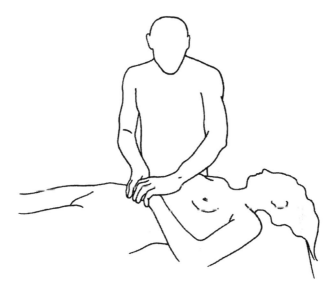

Fig. 79. Returning the Qi to the Source

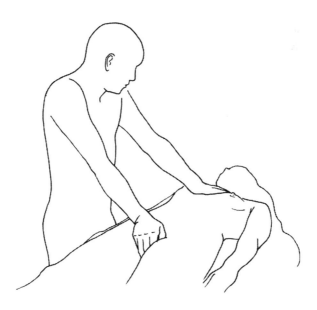

Fig. 80. Coming to Completion (Prayer)

Check In

While lying in Mountain Valley we can check in with our partner and see how she is doing or discuss how the session was for both of us.

Bathing the Goddess

We can then use warm moist towels to wipe the oil off the body of our partner. If we have prepared these warm, moist towels beforehand so much the better. If we like we can also draw her bath, bathe her, and put her to bed.

A COMMUNICATION RITUAL FOR INITIAL SEXUAL CONTACT

When two people become sexually involved for the first time there is the possibility for shadow and miscommunication to emerge, but also the opportunity for tremendous intimacy and growth. What follows is a ritual that is used after a decision has been made to become lovers but before sexual contact has actually taken place. The benefit of this exercise is that ritualizing the experience can enhance not only the quality of lovemaking but it can also enhance communication in the future. When we do this ritual we can avoid having to "read" signals from our partner or guess about where they are at.

The first two steps of the ritual, the Cleansing and the Clearing-Consecration, are identical to the Rivers of Love ritual described above.

The rest of the ritual is a way of communicating relevant information to our partner. We need not only do this the first time we make love, we can actually do it any time.

The ritual is as follows:

1) Cleansing Ourselves

2) Clearing and Consecrating the Room

When you sleep with someone you take off
a lot more than your clothes.

ANNA QUINDLEN

3) Engaging

> Fears
> Boundaries
> Desires
> Intention for our Partner

4) Communion

5) Resolution

> Mountain Valley
> Check In

6) Bathing

Cleansing, Clearing and Consecrating the Room

These preparations are the same as for the Rivers of Love ritual described above.

Engaging

As an herbalist, I sometimes teach classes on traditional plant gathering practices. When we gather herbs, we practice thinking from the head, speaking from the heart, and listening from the belly. This guideline may also serve us well as we are engage with our partner during this ritual.

When we engage, we sit naked across from our partner. If we like, we can sit together in a Lotus position. We sit in a way that is comfortable and from which we can speak clearly and see each other's eyes.

In engaging, we tell our partner our truth as it relates to making love and for our relationship. We share our fears, boundaries, desires, and intention for what we are creating together. One person speaks at a time. We can alternate between people for each section or each

When we talk about understanding, surely it takes place only when the mind listens completely, the mind being your heart, your nerves, your ears, when you give your whole attention to it.

person can cover them all before the other person speaks. Engaging can be done sitting or standing, but we prefer to do it sitting together naked while facing each other.

Fears

We describe our fears as regards this upcoming sexual encounter. We may have fears about having our lovemaking be misinterpreted, or fears of not being a good lover. We may have fears of getting a sexually transmitted disease. Whatever our fears may be this is a good time to put them on the table and discuss them.

Boundaries

We share boundaries with our partner. These could be related to monogamy, or safe sex, or anything else that we feel a need to communicate. A boundary could be that we need to be at the Post Office at 4:30, or that we do not like anal stimulation. Or, it could be that we need to use condoms or another form of birth control.

Desires

We share with our partner what we desire for the upcoming lovemaking, whatever that may be.

Intention for our Partner

In our intention we may express things similar to our desires, but we also may express our intention as regards what we want for our partner in this communion

Communion

We can proceed however we like, in a Rivers of Love session, or with whatever form of lovemaking that we choose.

Resolution

Mountain Valley

Getting back on the table, we can go into a Mountain Valley position with her head resting on our upper arm that is closest to the table, and our other arm is wrapped around her torso with one hand resting on her heart.

Check In

While lying in Mountain Valley we can check in with our partner and discuss how we are feeling.

Bathing

If we like we can share a bath or shower with our partner.

How you do anything is how you do everything.
ZEN SAYING

The tragedy of sexual intercourse is the perpetual virginity of the soul.
WILLIAM BUTLER YEATS

Infinity Practices

INFINITY PRACTICES: WEI WU WEI

W u *Wei* is a Chinese concept that means "non-action". *Wei Wu Wei* means "action within non-action". Wu Wei is a martial arts meditation that is powerful and profound. Wei Wu Wei from a Rivers of Love perspective is similar to this martial arts concept, but still significantly different. Wei Wu Wei, as we discuss it here involves the same level of awareness as traditional Wu Wei, but it is applied to our relationship, and to our senses.

Even within the context of this book, these Wei Wu Wei (Infinity) practices are different than other Rivers of Love practices. I have included them here because I believe that many couples may benefit from them.

When we do Infinity practices we are touching for the sheer experience of touch. We are touching to touch. In touching to touch, we open ourselves to new ways of experiencing intimacy. We agree to suspend any agenda we might have. We agree to hold space for each other and ourselves; to create a container for what we share. We remain suspended in the moment, engaged and vulnerable for an indefinite period of time. We allow ourselves to feel whatever it is that we are feeling, but we strive to remain in close physical contact.

We continue to hold space even if it becomes uncomfortable to do so. The closeness created in Infinity Practices will undoubtedly challenge us, which is good. They are designed to challenge us. We may find ourselves wanting to pull away, or become distracted with something else. When our discomfort emerges, we have two choices. We can move through the discomfort or we can break off contact.

We always have the option of breaking off contact and moving toward our distractions. But perhaps we can allow this discomfort to happen, to just allow ourselves to be uncomfortable without needing to fix it. Perhaps we can stretch ourselves and extend out through the discomfort. If so, this discomfort may become our teacher. It can become a container that can strengthen our character and shape our growth.

In this vulnerability some of our emotional patterns may emerge. Depending on whom we are and the nature of our relationship feelings that arise can be warm and comforting or as sharp as an ice pick. In relationships there tend to be both a "high desire" and a "low desire" partner. The high desire partner is sometimes characterized as needy or insecure. The low desire partner is sometimes characterized as being unable to commit or incapable of intimacy.

With Infinity practices we can engage our partner and have the opportunity to explore both high desire and low desire dynamics. It does not matter if we are the "high desire" or "low desire" partner, whether we are "top dog" or "bottom dog". The Infinity process is the same both ways; the roles we may find ourselves in are just two sides of the same coin. If we are the high desire partner we get to experience our neediness and clinginess first hand; and if we are the low desire partner we get to experience our claustrophobia and fear of being smothered.

Infinity practice allows each of us to find our own level and to be comfortable with it. It has the potential to change the "set point" of our intimacy.

An Infinity practice session has very little structure or format. It does not require any special bodywork or Qigong breathing skills. It is not a form of "Worshipping the Goddess". When we "Worship the

Goddess", we have an intention. In Infinity practice we deliberately suspend any intention we might have and pay attention to the immediacy of our senses. No one is "giving" and no one is "receiving"; we are both simply present. We notice what happens to us as we do it.

There are at least two potential benefits from doing Infinity practices:

The first benefit, for us as individuals, is that we get to experience clearly how we show up in our relationship. In touching to touch, we are exposed. We are exposed to our partner, but mostly we are exposed to ourselves. These Infinity practices, in stripping us bare, allow us to experience our emotional responses in a revealing way. If we are passive and self conscious in our relationship we will be passive and self-conscious in our Infinity practice. If we are needy and unable to stand on our own two feet, this will then become obvious to us. If we are irritable, we will become irritated. Our awareness can help show us where we need to deepen the roots in ourselves.

The second benefit, for us as a couple, is that we are able to experience touch just for the sheer pleasure of touching, and not as part of a larger agenda. Our touch does not have to go anywhere; it does not have to lead to something else. This awareness can reveal ways of communicating that we have not yet explored.

We fall into patterns in our sexuality, creating bedtime routines with our partner that we repeat endlessly. These routines create safe predictable ways for us to climax, or for our partner to climax. There is nothing wrong with these routines; familiarity and safety are important in lovemaking. But that which makes us feel safe can also smother us. Our safety can become a *trap* and our routines can become an *agenda*. Our agenda can create boredom, stagnation and possibly even resentment in our lovemaking; our partner may begin to feel used. Indeed many of our sexual patterns are designed to *avoid* deep intimacy. Our sexual routines, ironically, can keep us from experiencing closeness. If we want to create true intimacy we must be willing to stretch. We must step out of our patterns and move into spontaneity.

Infinity practice is the perfect vehicle through which to experience pure spontaneity. It gives us the opportunity of connecting with our partner in unpredictable ways.

If we really want to experience intimacy in our relationships we must root in ourselves. Infinity practice can facilitate that rooting. It can be a cornerstone in our foundation of intimate fulfillment. Doing Infinity practices, we may uncover parts of ourselves and terrains of intimacy that we never knew existed.

Infinite Embrace (Wei Wu Wei Holding)

More than any other infinity practice, Infinite Embrace can create discomfort and leave us feeling vulnerable. In Infinite Embrace we stand holding our partner for an indefinite period of time. We can be clothed or naked, but being clothed is more interesting in terms of what it brings up.

We stand with our partner with our feet between theirs, and we just stay there. We observe our need to cling, or reject, our partner. We notice the way she smells, the feel of her clothing, the way her body is balanced in our arms.

We watch our emotional reactions and our ability or inability to relax and connect. When we practice infinite embrace, our discomfort becomes our teacher.

Infinite Kiss (Wei Wu Wei Kissing)

In Infinite Kissing we allow our mouths to become sensual organs that explore our partner's lips and even parts of her face. We do not explore her lips for our pleasure, or for her pleasure, but just to explore. We are not chasing arousal, although arousal may happen. As we allow our kiss to become infinite, we become lost in the swirling moist embrace of our lovers mouth. Once we have learned to immerse ourselves in our lover's lips without agenda we may become addicted. We may find ourselves missing whole days of work due to this exercise.

Infinite Touch (Wei Wu Wei Naked)

In Infinite Touch we explore the whole of our body and that of our partner without agenda. Typically this is done lying side-by-side, with no one on top, and without oil. The lights are on and our eyes are open. We face each other in a "scissors" position so that each person is relaxed with their legs intertwined. (See *Infinite Touch Position*) It can also be done from one of the other positions, but it is important is that both partners begin from a comfortable position and it is helpful if the partners can look into each other's eyes.

In Infinite Touch, we begin with a Soft Entry, if possible (see *Soft Entry*). If not, we can simply lie with our genitals touching. After we are in position, we lie quietly and look at each other. From this position we allow our eyes, hands and emotions to explore what ever arises. Sex does not matter, erections do not matter, and orgasms do not matter. If erections, sex, or orgasms happen, there is no problem, but we do not pursue them. We do not chase pleasure. We allow ourselves to stay present and give our partner and ourselves the gift of an encounter without an agenda. Wei Wu Wei is open ended. This gift of openness is the heart of Wei Wu Wei.

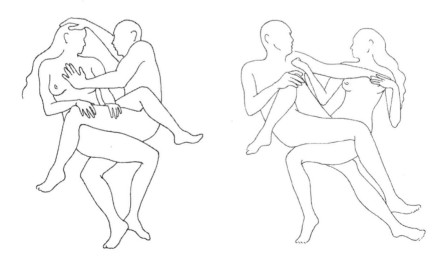

Fig. 80 & 81. Infinite Touch Positions

My religion is to live and die without regret.

JETSUN MILAREPA (1052 - 1135 CE)

Conclusions

The way we show up in our lives is the way we show up in our relationships ... and in our lovemaking. At birth and throughout childhood we are not all dealt the same hand, but it is how we play our hand as an adult that matters. Ultimately we choose how we show up and the circumstances from which our lives emerge. In our striving for integrity and happiness each of us brings different skills and challenges to the task. But for us as men, the task remains the same: to face the world and ourselves with tenacity and compassion.

I believe that these practices, internal and external, psychological and sexual, alone and with our partner, can benefit us as our lives open, deepen, and ripen.

This is not an easy path for us to take, but we, and our families, deserve no less.

Love, but love well.

APPENDIX

Do this exercise when you are alone, *not when your partner is in the room.*

Circle the top 15 values that you most want in a partner. Prioritize these values numbering them from 1 to 15 in the left hand column. Write in any values of your own that are not on the list.

So if persistence and creativity are both core values of yours,

Relationship Values

Priority	Relationship Value	Prioritized Relationship Value	Partner	Comments
____	**Dependability**	1. _____	____	_____
____	**Maturity**	2. _____	____	_____
____	**Wealth**	3. _____	____	_____
____	**Empathy**	4. _____	____	_____
____	**Integrity**	5. _____	____	_____
____	**Kindness**	6. _____	____	_____
____	**Fun**	7. _____	____	_____
____	**Passion for Life**	8. _____	____	_____
____	**Strength**	9. _____	____	_____
____	**Gentleness**	10. _____	____	_____
____	**Health**	11. _____	____	_____
____	**Sensitivity**	12. _____	____	_____
____	**Supportive**	13. _____	____	_____
____	**Loyalty**	14. _____	____	_____
____	**Stability**	15. _____	____	_____
____	**Intelligence**	16. _____	____	_____
____	**Adventurousness**	17. _____	____	_____
____	**Strong Sex Drive**	18. _____	____	_____
____	**Creativity**	19. _____	____	_____
____	**Physically Attractive**	20. _____	____	_____
____	**Sense of Humor**	21. _____	____	_____
____	**Good Parent**	22. _____	____	_____
____	**Attentive**	23. _____	____	_____
____	**Traditional Gender Roles**	24. _____	____	_____
____	**Sexy**	25. _____	____	_____
____	**Compassionate**	26. _____	____	_____
____	**Persistant**	27. _____	____	_____
____	**Safe Emotionally**	28. _____	____	_____
____	**Intellectually Stimulating**	29. _____	____	_____
____	**Trustworthiness**	30. _____	____	_____
____	**Socially Conscious**	31. _____	____	_____
____	**Compatible Scent**	32. _____	____	_____
____	**Good Lover**	33. _____	____	_____
____	**Hard Worker**	34. _____	____	_____
____	_____	35. _____	____	_____
____	_____	36. _____	____	_____
____	_____	37. _____	____	_____

ask yourself, "If I could only have one or the other, which would I choose?" Then place them in order with the more important value on top.

Write your prioritized values in the column provided under Prioritized Relationship Values.

Values can change over time; so do not worry about getting everything perfect. You can always go back and change it later.

Beginning with value #15 on your prioritized values list, work your way up from the bottom and ask yourself the following question for each value: *If I had the absolute perfect partner for me in all ways, but that partner did not have this value, would I stay in that relationship?*

As you work your way up the list, you will eventually come to a value for which the answer to that question is "no". In other words you would agree that, "*If I had the perfect partner for me but she did not manifest this value, I would leave the relationship*". Draw a line across the values list just below that value. All the values above this line are your core relationship values.

Then, under the "partner" heading, rate your partner on a 1 to 10 scale in terms of how much she manifests this value. Comment if you like about what this rating may mean for your relationship.

Some values, such as sense of humor or intelligence *might* be supplied outside of the relationship if everything else is reasonably lined up, but this can be challenging to navigate. And things like sexiness as a core value in a monogamous relationship do not lend themselves well to outside explorations.

This list is a blueprint of the core information you need in order to effectively navigate your relationship. The completed list can illuminate parts of your shadow and help you understand what is negotiable in your relationship and what is not.

This list can also be downloaded as a pdf file at:
www.davidbruceleonard.com/relationshipvalues.pdf

Resources

Chia, Mantak & Michael Winn. 1984. *Taoist Secrets of Love: Cultivating Male Sexual Energy*. Santa Fe: Aurora Press. *A classic on Daoist sexuality.*

Désilets, Saida. 2007. *Emergence of the Sensual Woman: Awakening Our Erotic Innocence.* Jade Goddess Publishing. Wailea, Hawai'i.

Kiely, Lorin.
http://www.topdownyoga.com
Cutting edge information on alterative modes of awareness and corresponding physiology.

Lanier, Tripp. The New Man.
http://personallifemedia.com/podcasts/238-the-new-man
Tripp Lanier's Podcast interviews for men.

Levine, Peter A. *Waking the Tiger : Healing Trauma : The Innate Capacity to Transform Overwhelming Experiences.* 1997. Berkeley, CA:

North Atlantic Books.
Adrenal-based trauma resolution.

ManKind Project.
http://www.mkp.org/
Powerful tools for male self-confrontation and transformation.

Masters, Robert Augustus. 2009. *Meeting the Dragon: Ending Our Suffering by Entering Our Pain.* Tehmenos Press.
http://www.robertmasters.com
Excellent information on how to navigate our emotions.

Quinn, Peyton. 2004. *Freedom from Fear: Taking Back Control of Your Life and Dissolving Depression.* PO Box 535. Lake George, Colorado 80827.
Adrenal-based trauma resolution. Self-defense oriented.

Schnarch, David. 1997; *Passionate Marriage: Keeping Love and Intimacy Alive in Committed Relationships.* New York: W. W. Norton & Company.
http://passionatemarriage.com/
A classic in the field and still very timely.

Biography and Contact Information

David Bruce Leonard is a deep ecologist, body-worker, Qigong practitioner, acupuncturist, martial artist, and plant lover. He has studied medicine with teachers in Asia, North and South America, and Hawai'i.

David believes that our health and the meaning of our lives are inseparable from our interactions with the natural world.

He has worked in a bank, done marine whale research, and has been seen in public attempting to dance Argentine tango.

David is available for workshops and consultations in the creation of men's groups and support circles. Private coaching sessions for men or couples are available. He can be reached via his website www.DavidBruceLeonard.com.

29178178R00150

Made in the USA
Columbia, SC
28 October 2018